CW00408988

Pamela B.
(Fakenham
Norfolk.)

How to Live Safely in a Dangerous World

How to Live Safely in a Dangerous World

The Essential, Practical Guide

by
Simon Romain

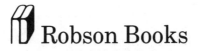 Robson Books

First published in Great Britain in 1989 by Robson Books Ltd,
Bolsover House, 5-6 Clipstone Street, London W1P 7EB.

Copyright 1989 Simon Romain

British Library Cataloguing in Publication Data

Romain, Simon
  How to live safely in a dangerous world
  1. Self-defence, Manuals
  I. Title
  613.6'6

ISBN 0 86051 565 6

Printed in Great Britain by
St Edmundsbury Press Ltd, Bury St Edmunds, Suffolk

To
my mother and father

Acknowledgements

Many thanks to everyone who helped me put this book together: Andy and Ilana for modelling; Marlene for typing; Dave for his photography and graphic ideas; my father for his editorial efforts; Pete for his legal advice and, last but not least, Adrian for his time and effort behind, and in front of, the camera.

CONTENTS

INTRODUCTION

WHAT'S THIS THEN?

This book is written to interest you, make you laugh and share with you some very valuable information – information which you are unlikely to find in any other book. Its pages are filled with stories of real-life events involving all types of people. Some of the stories ended happily, others did not, but they are all true and each one in its own way makes a point.

So sit down in your favourite armchair, put up your feet and settle down to read about the neglected art of self-preservation in modern times.

1

THE BASIC RULES

Confucius, the ancient Chinese philosopher, once said that you should treat others in the way that you would like them to treat you. To my mind, that's a very good philosophy. Remember the hospitality of ancient times, when weary travellers would be welcomed in (sometimes) and given food, drink and a bed for the night, merely because they were strangers in a strange land?

Well, life has changed since then, and people now have to be a little bit wary when they meet strangers or find themselves in unusual places or situations. I use my words carefully here: 'wary' does not mean 'paranoid'. 'Wary' means being aware of what is going on around you; being paranoid is something entirely different.

For example, let's say an old lady with a walking stick approaches you in the High Street and asks you the way to the nearest public toilets. If you, fearing an attack by an octogenarian mugger, floor her with a swift knee to the stomach, then it can reasonably be said that you are, without doubt, paranoid. This is a condition which should be avoided by all self-preservation enthusiasts. You can be aware of what is going on around you and yet treat everyone you meet in a polite, friendly and respectful way. If anyone demonstrates that they don't intend to behave likewise, then your attitude can change. Until then, Confucius is your best bet.

Always bear in mind that self-defence is not a martial art, nor is it unarmed combat. (Martial arts are a way of life – skills learnt and practised over a long period, used to tune the mind and body to a state of superb readiness. Unarmed combat is basically the quickest way of attacking somebody and grinding them into little pieces before moving on to your next victim.) Self-defence is really a First Aid Preservation Kit. Like first aid, it cannot guarantee that you are going to be all right but it can certainly help you improve your chances.

Self-defence is the art of self-preservation and that does not mean just fighting to protect yourself. It means avoiding trouble, recognizing trouble before trouble recognizes you, and getting out of trouble by using your wits and not just your fists. In the final analysis of course, if your back is to the wall and you have to fight, then that is also self-defence. Fighting is always a last resort, because the result is never certain; and if we do fight, we have a responsibility to use our knowledge only to get us out of trouble – not for revenge or retribution.

This involves a different type of responsibility as well, and to accept it takes real courage. We have to accept that each of us is responsible for our own preservation. Very few others will help us. Three male actors, two big and one small, once staged an experiment in the Champs-Elysées, that magnificent wide road running down from the Arc de Triomphe in Paris. Hundreds of people sit at cafés on the pavement on either side of the road enjoying the sights. The two large men chased the smaller man, caught him and then proceeded to bash his brains out in front of everyone at the tables – or so it seemed. The smaller man writhed on the ground in authentic agony, screaming and calling for help as the two bigger men pounded him with their feet and fists – an expert job, I must say.

It may surprise you to learn that not one single person came to the help of that poor little man who was apparently being so brutally attacked. Not only did some people continue to read their newspapers, but others actually gathered to watch! Now it's fair enough to be cautious when two big men are attacking somebody else, but I wouldn't say it was unreasonable to expect someone to make a telephone call and alert the police. Would you?

Don't ever rely on anybody coming to your aid; you may be lucky but don't count on it. In the end, it's down to you. The basic rules of self-defence are quite simple: keep your eyes open and you can usually avoid trouble. If you can't avoid trouble, then throw valour to the winds and run. Remember that old saying about living to fight another day? If you can't run – maybe you are taking your grandmother for a walk – then you have to deter the 'nasties' using whatever method seems best at the time. You'll need plenty of courage to face up to the fact that trouble is about to strike and then to deter whoever is behind it. You'll need stamina to run or to fight; and if you are reasonably strong, as well as courageous, then that will also help in any physical struggle. One other thing: *never* ever threaten anybody. Either walk or run away, or fight.

Let me tell you a story. Practising what I preach, I never threaten anybody. However, everyone comes unstuck once in a while, especially when caught unawares. I was walking through a busy suburb one evening with my girlfriend Jo. As we stepped into a side road, a car roared round the corner, its tyres screeching, and almost wiped both of us into oblivion. We got a tremendous shock of course and I was extremely upset because the love of my life had nearly been made part of the road surface. I ran after the car waving my fist and hurling abuse and insults, something I had never done before. The car, which was about 20 yards down the road, suddenly stopped; I watched, puzzled. Jo was some 10 yards behind me near the corner.

Suddenly, from out of the passenger seat, under the orange glow of the street lamps, arose an Adonis, at least 6 foot 3 inches tall with a V-shaped torso, long golden hair, and an immaculate white suit. He looked at me, calmly threw his jacket into the car and then launched into what I can only describe as the most unbelievable martial arts display II have ever seen. He was doing things I'd never even read about. And it was for my benefit – to show what he was about to do to me. For the first time ever, my pride got the better of me and I desperately looked round for some means of defending myself. If there had been a loose lamp-post in sight I probably would have grabbed that. There was nothing.

Suddenly, salvation: Jo took hold of my arm and dragged me away, giving several extremely good reasons why we should leave as soon as possible. Honour having been saved, I for one was certainly not going to argue but, just for good measure, I hurled a few more insults back at the towering colossus who was marching towards us. As we got round the corner, Jo and I took one look at each other and ran. So much for heroism. But there's a moral to the story: *never* threaten anybody. Either leave or wallop them; one or the other.

2
TAKING PRECAUTIONS

In many ways, self-defence is like family planning: if you take precautions, you'll often save yourself a lot of trouble. Avoiding trouble in self-defence terms does not mean lying low and limiting your lifestyle. All you have to do is be alert and take those few basic precautions. A word of warning though: taking steps to avoid trouble does help but it can't guarantee safety.

Awareness

The first thing to do is keep your eyes open. It is quite amazing how much the human eye actually misses when we walk from place to place. When you next walk down your road, have a really good look around. Have a close look at everything, from lamp-posts to houses. Look up at the rooftops and you will see things you have never noticed before. Look past the buildings and you will see buildings in the background or on the horizon that you didn't know existed. I suggest this as a purely private exercise. (I don't think it would go down too well in Oxford Circus during the rush hour.) It will certainly make you see how much you do not see, and then you can decide how much you want to see in the future. It's really up to you. Personally, I have a basic level of awareness which I raise if I find myself in a place or situation which could prove a problem. Remember, you have to remain sociable; staring at people is the quickest way to earn a free bed in the local hospital.

Unfortunately trouble often comes when you're least expecting it. A group of us were eating in a restaurant at a big hotel off the Strand a couple of years ago. We were having a great time and feeling very relaxed. My girlfriend had put her handbag between her feet under

13

her chair so that no one could pinch it. As we chatted and laughed, I noticed a man sitting just behind us on a small staircase that led to another part of the restaurant; he was holding an umbrella. I forgot about him and carried on eating until, half an hour later, my girlfriend realized that her handbag had disappeared. We turned round but the man on the staircase had vanished.

Now that I think about it, his behaviour had been a little odd. I mean, what was he doing on the staircase anyway? I'm certain he'd hooked his umbrella through the handles of the handbag and pulled it out, right under our very eyes. He had then calmly walked out of the restaurant and into the night. There's no need to be paranoid but sometimes it does take a conscious effort to be aware of what is going on around you.

Body Language

While you are looking around, one of the earliest indications of any danger will be the behaviour of those around you. Some people call it 'body language' – the non-verbal signals which every human shows throughout the day. Our facial expressions, our hand gestures, the way we hold our arms and body, and whether or not we make eye contact – all of these give out messages, sometimes to supplement our voices and sometimes instead of them. All of us are experts in body language; we give it out and receive it, and have been doing so since the day we were born. Most of the signals are only noted subconsciously but, with a little effort, it is quite easy to become more aware of them so that, should a warning bell ring at the back of your head, you will know it is time to be careful.

I'm not going to write about body language in detail because there are already several books on the subject (see page 120). The important point is that a basic awareness of body language enables us not only to recognize danger signals from other people but also to tell those around us that we don't intend to submit meekly to being attacked. For example, ask yourself the following questions:
When you walk along the street, do you walk decisively with your head up, looking around you?
When you speak to strangers or acquaintances you meet, do you
   (a) look them in the eye?
   (b) nervously look away?
Do you
   (a) fidget with your hands, shift from foot to foot or find your voice quavering?
   (b) stand relaxed and speak with confidence?

Alert

Asleep

A nutcase!

Attackers are always on the lookout for a potential victim, someone who will succumb easily. They look for clues and note carefully how we carry ourselves. You don't have to be aggressive to appear confident; you don't have to dominate the High Street pavement, take massive strides or swing your arms. If you want to see how you look to others, ask a friend to film you on video as you walk along. The video is a cruel critic and will immediately show whether you appear to be a victim or a survivor.

Often our intuition or sixth sense warns us of impending danger but we ignore it because of social pressure, lack of time or lack of courage. Given our expertise in body language, which plays a large part in such intuitive forebodings, we ignore these warnings at our peril. Our intuition – linked to that strongest of instincts, survival – is often more accurate than logic or reason. Cultivate intuition but beware of neurosis.

Unfortunately, such knowledge of human behaviour works against us as well. We can't hide our signals – including lack of confidence – from other humans. Have you ever been speaking to someone, perhaps an attractive member of the opposite sex, when, without thinking, you've looked down at their mouth? Maybe you find their lips attractive or you are anxious to see what their teeth are like but, never mind, you did it. It only took an instant, yet when you look back into their eyes you know that they know that you did it, and you know that they know that you know that they know!

If you do take the time to read a book on body language, be warned: a lot of it is theory, and theories are often wrong. Generally, if you keep an open mind, and do not become too engrossed in the technicalities, you will pick up danger signals fairly quickly, should they come your way.

Travelling on Foot

Body language is with us night and day but something else which takes up a fair amount of time in our lives is travel. Throughout the day, we are travelling from one place to another – sometimes round the corner, sometimes round the world – on foot, by car, bus, train, taxi, ship, horse or plane. Apart from the way in which we carry ourselves (i.e. our body language), there are a few basic precautions which we can take to improve our safety when travelling. Put yourself in the position of a potential attacker and you will see how effective they are. For example, ask yourself the following questions: When you walk down the street, do you walk

    (a) facing the oncoming traffic?
    (b) with the traffic?

Do you walk
- (a) in the middle of the pavement?
- (b) near the edge of the pavement by the road?
- (c) close to the buildings on the pavement?
- (d) in the road?

If you look at any good policeman, you will notice that he always walks facing the traffic, so that he can see what is coming towards him and is not taken by surprise. Walking near doorways or the kerb

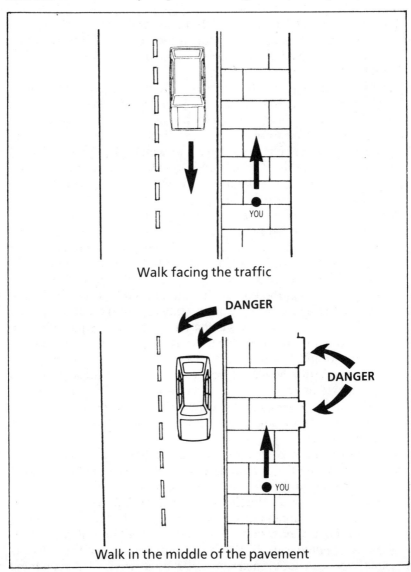

Walk facing the traffic

Walk in the middle of the pavement

puts you within range of a hidden attacker or a parked car. Wandering in the road, although giving you good all-round vision, puts you at the mercy, even late at night, of the local juggernaut or aspiring Grand Prix racer. The best place to walk is in the middle of the pavement.

Ask yourself some more questions:

When you go from A to B, do you

(a) plan your route, making sure that you stick to busy, well-lit streets?

(b) take short cuts across open ground or down unlit alleyways?

If you are forced to use a dingy side street, do you casually notice potential escape routes or sources of help like pubs, garages or occupied houses?

A few years ago, a young woman was brutally killed by a notorious murderer who was later brought to justice. She died because she took a short cut across waste ground even though she knew that the murderer was at large in that area. Had she gone the long way round, using a main road, she would only have added 10 minutes to her journey. On foot, in a lonely desolate area, pursued by a stronger and faster man armed with hideous weapons, the young girl had no chance of escape.

Even more recently, a young woman jogger was raped in an alleyway adjoining one of the biggest main roads in central London. She was out running, wearing a pair of headphones attached to a personal cassette recorder, and could not hear small sounds around her because her ears and mind were filled with music. There had been several rapes in the London area at around that time and, sure enough, the attacker was waiting, hidden in the alley, for an unsuspecting and defenceless visitor. He let the girl jog past him and then jumped out on to her back; she never even heard him until his arms were around her body. Being in an alleyway with only two exits, she had little chance of escape; she was too shocked even to think of escape anyway. Of course, nobody saw or heard what was going on. She was raped and left. How many people do you see every day – cycling, walking and even driving – wearing headphones and singing to the music?

The clothes she was wearing were the only things in the jogger's favour: they were ideal for running or fighting. Obviously, we don't need to walk around in leotards or combat gear all day, but it is suicidal to wear clothes that impede our natural movement. When I see a woman in a long, tight, pencil skirt and high heels tottering down the road, I often wonder how fast she could run if chased. Or whether she could run at all? As usual, a happy compromise is possible: you can look smart and attractive while still remaining perfectly mobile. The attacker will always be dressed for the occasion; it is invariably the victim who is unprepared.

When moving from place to place, we often carry things. Heavy, bulky bags weigh you down and stop you moving your arms, so avoid carrying them if possible. If you have a bag, hold on to it as though you mean to keep it. Bags can work in our favour too. The old trick of bag-throwing is often used by criminals who, while carrying the proceeds of their latest project, are stopped by young policemen late at night.

'Hello,' says the constable, 'what do we have here?' The criminal replies, 'Have a look, mate!' as he throws the heavy bag straight at the bobby, knocking him backwards on to the pavement. The bag opens and the 'swag' from the previous night's job spills on to the pavement: gold candlesticks, war trophies and silverware. Meanwhile the burglar is running for his life in the opposite direction, cursing his luck but safe in the knowledge that he will live to steal another day. It's a good move, and worth remembering.

The army may not be the safest organization to join but they really know their stuff when it comes to travel – or 'patrolling' as they call it. They always find out as much as possible about the areas through which they move, and we can do the same. Get to know the places you often visit: notice who uses these places and what activities go on there.

For example, go to Piccadilly Circus in London and see the statue of Eros, bow in hand and still balancing on one foot after all this time. You will no doubt be dazzled by the flashing neon lights and impressed by the crowds, the bustling traffic, the tall Victorian and Georgian buildings, the red buses and black taxis. At least those are the things a tourist would notice. If you really know the area, you will see a completely different picture: drug dealers, addicts, pimps, prostitutes, muggers, policemen in unmarked cars, plain-clothes policemen, illegal gambling on the pavement, drinking clubs and gathering places for male prostitutes, skinheads and petty criminals. Put in context, these people do not dominate the scene, but it is good to be aware of them. If you can gather this type of information about the areas you frequent, it will be much easier to avoid trouble when it occurs. As everybody knows, it is always the tourists who are robbed, conned and cheated first.

Soldiers are also very much on the ball when it comes to 'night vision'. On the battlefield, a night patrol about to scout out the lie of the land, or mount a surprise attack, obviously cannot afford to stumble around with flashlights pointing in all directions. So how do they manage? Well, they see with their ears. If you stay still, you can hear other people moving towards you long before they can see you.

Within 15 minutes the human eye begins to become accustomed to the dark – provided it is not blinded by light, in which case, you have to start all over again. After about 40 minutes the process is complete and you will be able to see some things in great detail even in the blackest night.

In built-up areas, the problem is cars and street lights. Street lights are not too bad because they don't shine directly into your face and only cast a fairly soft light. Car headlamps are a different matter: they wreck night vision immediately. The simple answer is to close the same eye whenever a car approaches; that is your 'night eye'. Now, whatever you do, do not walk down Oxford Street at 11 o'clock at night, when the pavements are thronged with people and the roads are bursting with cars, with one eye tightly shut. Everyone will either sympathize with your terrible squint or think that you are offering some form of invitation. No, this technique is only to be used when travelling home alone, late at night, through fairly deserted streets. Next time you are in the countryside, spend 15 minutes in the dark, or, better still, half an hour. You will be be amazed by what you can see. Night vision is a powerful weapon available to every night traveller and, although not so effective in areas lit by street lights, it is still an essential part of your survival kit.

Travelling by Car

Any self-defence book will list all the basic precautions for car travel. Essentially, the vulnerable times are the beginning and end of each journey, although danger can strike at any time. An attacker may break into your empty car and hide behind the front seats, or wait for you to fumble for your car keys as you approach. He may deflate one of your tyres and attack as you crouch over it, or wait until you leave your car, and then pounce as you feel around for your house keys. So check your car and the area around it before you get in, check that the tyres and windows are intact, and have your house or car keys in your hand long before you need them. Make sure that you always park your car in busy, well lit streets, within running distance of houses and shops and clear of natural hiding places like trees and low walls.

As anyone who has survived an accident will tell you, the apparent security of cars is deceptive. From our point of view, the illusion of solidity is just as dangerous. Even with the doors locked, determined attackers can still break in and drag you out if you cannot drive away. Do you remember those two off-duty British soldiers who drove into an IRA funeral cortège by mistake in Northern Ireland?

When the angry mourners realized who they were, the men were dragged out, beaten and shot with their own pistols. Their chances of survival vanished the moment they stumbled into the procession; one wrong turn and that was it.

That was an extreme case, and unlikely to happen in England, unless you drive into a full-scale riot in one of the inner-city areas. But attackers have hijacked cars waiting at traffic lights and road junctions by simply opening the passenger door, jumping in and forcing the driver to a more deserted area. I speak from experience!

Driving home one night at about 11 o'clock, through a fairly rough area, I stopped at a zebra crossing. Suddenly, from out of the shadows, a man ran towards my car, yanked open the passenger door and jumped in, taking me completely by surprise. He was tall, fairly well-built and unkempt, with long brown hair and stubble on his chin. His clothes were quite scruffy and he looked a complete villain. He was frightened, very frightened. Putting his hand inside his dirty bomber jacket, he drew out a long, thick kitchen knife and put it on the dashboard. He wanted me to drive on and I was in no position to argue. But I was lucky. All he wanted was a 'getaway car' to take him away from the zebra crossing as fast as possible because, when he jumped into my life, he was being chased by a whole gang armed with crossbows and intent on target practice.

A mile down the road, he asked me to stop, jumped out and ran off into the darkness, leaving his knife behind. I drove to the nearest police station, handed in the knife and told the desk sergeant my story. Sure enough, over the police radio came the news that a gang had been seen roaming the area, armed with crossbows. My passenger had had a lucky escape that night; he had used his wits well and survived another fight. The next day I too rose a wiser man.

Jumping into cars is not the only way of earning a free lift. A friend of mine, Debbie, was once driving late at night through an unfamiliar area of London. Although using a road map, she managed to lose herself and so stopped to ask a young man the way. He was pleasant enough and told her all she needed to know. Just as Debbie was about to wind up the window, he suddenly asked her for a lift, saying he only lived 5 minutes down the road and could she drop him on her way? Debbie hesitated, wondering how she could refuse somebody who had just been so helpful; but she did. That took a lot of courage and I agree with her completely. She was alone, at night, in a deserted unfamiliar area, with a stranger whom she had only met 5 minutes before. If she had allowed him in, she would have been defenceless. The odds are that the young man would not have laid a finger on her, but what if ...?

How wonderful it must be to live in a community where everyone trusts their neighbours and even strangers; a community where you can invite outsiders into your house, garden or car, and share hospitality and friendship without any fear of danger. There are still places where that heavenly state of affairs exists, but not in London; nor in any of the cities or towns of what we call 'the civilized West'.

One last point: the Highway Code tells you to check your car before you drive to make sure that your lights are working, tyres inflated, petrol tank full, and so on. From a survivor's point of view,

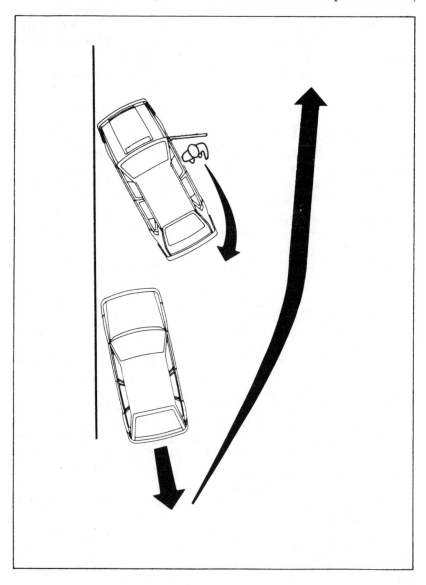

those are wise words. If you ever break down on a country road at 2 a.m., you will truly understand the meaning of the word 'alone'.

Not only are we vulnerable in our own cars, but other people can use their cars as weapons against us. Not long ago, my parents were driving home late at night when, for no apparent reason, a car full of men tried to force them off the road. My father simply drove to the nearest police station and the attackers vanished.

If someone ever does force you to stop by driving their car in front of yours, stay calm. Wait until the driver or the passenger has got out of the car and, as they approach you, quickly reverse back down the road so that you are out of their reach and have room to manoeuvre. Then zoom off, leaving them standing by the roadside. Whether you lose them or not, go straight to the nearest source of help and ring the police. Write down the registration number and description of the car and driver or passenger as soon as possible before you forget.

On the subject of hitch-hiking, many self-defence books advise that it is safe to pick up hitch-hikers or to hitch-hike yourself in certain circumstances. I disagree and think that a lone driver should never give lifts to strangers. If they are obviously in trouble, you can stop down the road at a garage or pub and phone for help. In the same way, single travellers should never hitch-hike even when stranded. If this happens at night, go to ground, shelter yourself as best you can and go looking for help the next day unless you're likely to freeze to death in the meantime. There is a big difference between hardship and danger, and I'll take hardship any day.

Taxis and Minicabs

Having said that, we do in fact climb into strange cars regularly. The only difference is that they are called taxis. But who drives the taxis? To drive a London black cab, you have to pass stringent geographical and driving tests, so you can be sure that any London cabbie knows what he is doing and where he is going. That does not automatically mean that his character is equally reliable. On the other hand, I've never read of any attack by a cab-driver in his cab. For a start, the licence number is plastered all over it so, unless he has stolen the taxi, it would be easy to trace him.

Minicabs are a different matter. As far as I know, the drivers supply the cars themselves, and only their licences are checked. So, again there is no guarantee of reliability or security. Most people never have any trouble so there is no need to be paranoid, but do be aware of the facts: the little word 'taxi' or 'minicab' written on a car is not necessarily an official certificate of good character.

Public Transport

At the other end of the scale there is public transport. Here there are often too many people (not too few) but safety does not lie in numbers, as we saw in the Champs-Elysées story. Experiments on the American subway system have proved once again that very few people will come to the rescue if you are attacked.

On the London Underground, a new phenomenon has recently appeared, known as 'steaming'. It's a very simple tactic: a gang of at least five or six young, strong, aggressive types select an isolated victim on a platform or in a train carriage, steam into them with fists and feet, rob them and steam away again. The attack is effective because it is so fast – a sort of mugger's 'blitzkrieg' – and the dust has usually settled before anyone even realizes what has happened. Steaming is not restricted to tube trains: it happens on buses, in shops and even department stores where large items are stolen *en masse* in broad daylight. At one point, the number of steaming attacks in Oxford Street reached such a peak that Scotland Yard formed a special squad to deal with it.

The possibility of being attacked on public transport is still low, especially if you avoid the more notorious stations, such as those in Central London and at the southern end of the Northern Line. All the same, whether on bus or train, stay within reach of an exit and other passengers, or, even better, the guard or driver. You cannot expect them to fight for you but their presence may deter the less determined thug. Protect your back and keep a casual eye on those around you.

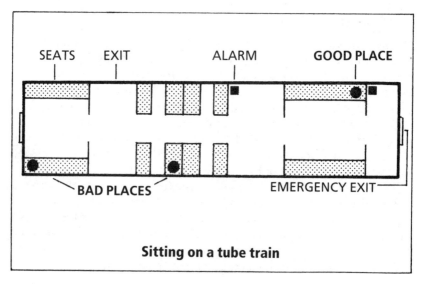

Sitting on a tube train

Alarms

Some people carry pocket alarms when they are out and about. Personally, I don't have much faith in them, especially those designed to alert the neighbourhood. Have you ever noticed the response when a car alarm goes off in a busy street? Everyone ignores it! Even those alarms that emit a piercing bleep to momentarily stun the attacker lack the visual impact of a screaming human. I prefer to use the voice to stun, not only for that reason, but also because it is almost always immediately available. You don't have to fish for it in your pocket as you see trouble coming.

Careless Talk

Still on the subject of voice, let me remind you of the slogan which heralded the government's campaign against German spies in England during the Second World War. 'The walls have ears,' they said. That still applies today. When you are chatting in a public place, be careful not to give away sensitive information about your personal movements, holiday plans, valuables or your house, just in case some unwelcome eavesdropper is enthusiastically tuning into your conversation.

As for houses, I am not going to touch on their security here, but merely suggest that you contact the Crime Prevention Officer at your local police station. He should give you an excellent list of precautions to take, and explain the benefits of starting a Neighbourhood Watch Scheme in your road. By the way, friendly, protective neighbours are absolutely invaluable and well worth cultivating for that reason if no other.

This chapter is about taking precautions. Unfortunately, every now and then, trouble may come and find us, no matter what we do, and then we have to stand and face it. That is what the rest of this book is all about.

3
THE LAW

Perched on top of the Central Criminal Court in London stands a golden statue. With a sword in one hand and a pair of scales in the other, it symbolizes British justice and law – and the law has quite a lot to say about self-defence.

Defending Yourself

The law books allow us only to use 'such force as is reasonably necessary' to get out of trouble, but the legal definition of 'reasonable force' appears to be quite wide. There are a few basic guidelines. If someone comes looking for trouble, you are expected to decline his or her offer and give that person a chance to back off. But if fighting appears inevitable, you don't have to wait to be hit first. Should someone attack you with a tennis racket and you calmly blast them with a shotgun, then you legally become unreasonable. And once the threat of attack is over, you must stop fighting. It is no good claiming self-defence if, having beaten your attacker to the ground, you then decide to go back and stamp all over his or her helpless body. If you fight, there is always the risk of prosecution or a civil claim for damages. And if you go over the top the police could charge you with various types of assault, depending on the damage done.

I remember picking up a discarded newspaper and reading about a vicious gang attack on two young men, one of whom managed to escape. Looking back, he saw that the gang were pounding his fallen friend with lumps of concrete so he decided to help by jumping into his car and driving at full speed towards them. They scattered in terror. He saved his friend and I don't know whether he managed to run down any of the gang. All the same, he ended up in court, charged with assault. The questions being argued in the courtroom were these: could the defendant claim that driving his car at the gang was self-defence, given that he had already escaped? Or could he claim that he was defending his friend with reasonable force?

We are legally allowed to fight when protecting ourselves, our family, or when enforcing the law itself. A gang beating someone senseless with concrete is committing grievous bodily harm – a serious offence with an immediate public power of arrest. Everyone watching has the right (some would say obligation) to step in and arrest the attackers. If, as is likely, the attackers turn nasty, the arresting citizen is quite entitled to use a reasonable amount of force to defend himself and restrain them until the police arrive. So was it reasonable for the driver to step in and use his car to defend himself against a gang armed with lumps of concrete? I'll never know what happened to him because the bottom part of the paper was missing – and I wonder whether his friend recovered.

Defending Your Property

The law also allows us to fight to defend our property. There was a case where a householder escaped a claim for civil damages after he had stabbed an intruder with a bayonet! Hearing noises downstairs, he got out of bed, picked up his bayonet and went to investigate. The householder claimed that the burglar had jumped him in the dark and so he had stabbed him. The burglar not only lost his civil action against the owner but was also presumably convicted at the local criminal courts – it just wasn't his lucky day. Be warned; legal cases do not always go the householder's way, so put away the shotgun and do not get angry when people drop litter on your front lawn.

Carrying Weapons

Criminals carry weapons while we do not. Since they are working on the wrong side of the law anyway, they're not too worried. But if we get caught, our lives can be traumatically affected. A train commuter, a middle-aged respectable type, was recently attacked by a young bully and, in self-defence, stabbed him with a swordstick. The commuter was prosecuted, found guilty of carrying an offensive weapon, and fined. All the newspapers carried the story and there was a wave of public sympathy for him. To add insult to injury, the young thug filed a civil claim against Mr Respectable for wounding him and, although he won his action, the damages awarded were only nominal, reflecting the spirit and not the letter of the law.

Apart from the Firearms and Public Order Acts, which are both specific, it is the Prevention of Crime Act 1953 and the Criminal Justice Act 1988 that are mainly used to prosecute weapon carriers. Under the 1953 Act, it is an offence to carry a weapon in a public place unless you have permission or a good reason, and the onus is on the carrier to show that they have one or the other. The vital point to note is that arming to defend yourself is not a good reason in the eyes of the law. The Act defines three types of offensive weapon: 'made' (such as a bayonet) for killing or wounding; 'adapted' (like a smashed milk bottle) so that it becomes a weapon; or 'intended' (such as a penknife or empty bottle) which was not designed or adapted as a weapon but could be used if the need arose. It's up to the police to prove the necessary intent when the weapon falls into that last category.

If you are on a camping holiday and are stopped with a penknife or sheath knife on your belt and a rucksack on your back, most policemen would accept that you need the knife for camping. That may not go down so well in the middle of Leicester Square if you are wearing a suit. A friend of mine, a policeman, once stopped a huge wrestler late at night. In fact the wrestler was a well-known stuntman. He was absolutely colossal – about 5 foot 10 inches tall and 6 foot wide, and carrying a riding crop covered from end to end with thick black tape. My friend asked him why he was carrying the crop. The monster looked at him and, realizing what the policeman was thinking, growled slowly, 'If I want to tear people to pieces, I don't need a little stick.' The point was taken, intention was disproved and the man was left to go on his way.

The 1988 Act goes even further, saying that it is an offence to carry any blade – (except a pocket knife with a folding blade whose cutting edge is not longer than three inches) or sharp point in a public place without 'good reason' or 'lawful authority'. You can claim other defences as well: for example, if you need the blade or point for work, or if it is necessary to carry it for religious reasons or as part of any national costume. As under the 1953 Act, the onus of proving that we have good reason, lawful authority, or one of the other defences, rests squarely with us.

Knives are now a standard part of the criminal's equipment and it is very difficult for us to defend ourselves without going beyond the law, but there are ways – as you will see later. Until then, bear in mind the spirit of the law: use reasonable force to defend yourself, but only when you must. The statue at the Old Bailey may not be able to speak, but she is not dumb.

4
GETTING YOUR BODY INTO GEAR

The body is a machine – an extremely powerful machine too – pounding away day and night to keep us going in top gear, and capable of withstanding serious damage. Everyone wants to avoid ill-health and the limitations that go with it but, like all good machines, the body needs to be lovingly tuned and oiled. Being fit and healthy is especially important if you have to fight your way out of trouble or run for home.

I remember once having to chase a man who had done something nasty to someone, and losing him in the darkness as he dashed down a cobbled mews. Running on, I saw a dim shape kneeling on the ground a few yards ahead of me. There he was, gasping for breath, his chest heaving and his belly hanging over his belt, as he struggled to recover from the tremendous exertion of 2½ minutes of running. He was in such a state that I literally had to drag him back to the main road. It turned out that he was a heavy drinker and smoker, who had not been running for about the last 20 years. So fitness is important, and how much we do is up to each one of us. But it's unwise to take our bodies to the Grand Prix circuit of running for our lives without doing a few practice laps first.

If you go to the parks in Peking early in the morning, you will see hundreds of people gently exercising for health and longer life. The emphasis is on the word 'gentle', and that's a good idea first thing in the morning, because the body does not like being rudely awakened from a deep sleep by 50 press-ups and a sprint round the block. It tends to go on strike by pulling a muscle or twisting a joint. Very gentle exercise is, on the other hand, an excellent way of waking up.

I used to do a job which involved getting up at an unearthly hour while, as far as I could tell, the rest of the world slept. Not only that, but, because of the nature of the work, I had to be 100 per cent alert and ready for any type of trouble from the moment I turned up. I used to stagger off to work like a complete zombie until I decided to take a lesson from the Chinese.

All you have to do is gently move all your joints, several times, one after the other; carefully stretch and then tense your muscles;

Here are some of those early-morning exercises

Joints. Circle your hips slowly and
rhythmically, first one way and then the other

Massage. Invigorate your shoulder muscles
and skin with soft massage

breathe deeply, but not too deeply, and invigorate your body by
massaging it with your hands, someone else's hands or a rough
towel. Every movement should be slow and gentle. The effect is
absolutely amazing and the whole thing only takes about 10 or 15
minutes from start to finish. It's immensely enjoyable to feel those
tingling currents of energy beginning to flow all over you. Ten
minutes of light movement and your body is in gear and your mind in
the driving seat.

When talking about fitness, I mean the basic amount of exercise
necessary to keep our bodies in working order, not activities like
athletics, weight-lifting, assault courses or long-distance running.
Personally, I exercise and run about three times a week, early in the
morning. I take it very slowly and easily; in fact I relax and enjoy it.
The more relaxed you are, the more freely your body can move.
Keep your exercises plain and simple, and you have a better chance
of enjoying them, rather than looking on them as a burden. And the
more enjoyable they are, the more regularly you will do them. Once
again, if you really are determined to get fitter, go to a good
bookshop and choose any one of the myriad of books on the subject
(see page 120).

There are a few basic guidelines for exercising: first, moderation is

Stretching. Gently reach up

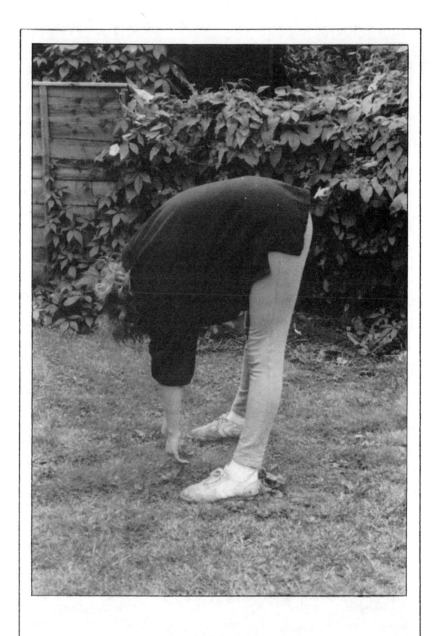

Slowly hang down

Breathing. Breathe in and out – not too
deeply, expanding both the top and bottom
of the rib cage

Muscle-tensing. Raise your knee to exercise
the upper leg and hip muscles

Vertical press-ups to stimulate the shoulders,
chest, back and arms

A final stretch for your back using yoga postures.

The 'cat'

The 'coil'

the name of the game. Warm up your body before you start anything strenuous and avoid pushing yourself too hard or too fast during exercise. Don't suddenly stop moving at the end of a training session. Your body needs to return to its normal pace slowly, just as it must be warmed up. It is a good idea not to eat for an hour or two beforehand, or you may end up with some serious indigestion. For toning up the whole body and increasing your stamina, swimming and running are both excellent. Running is extremely relevant because one day you may really need to do it. Road-running jars the spine and leg joints, so a visit to the soft green of the local park is much better – but be careful where you tread. Traditional exercises like sit-ups, press-ups and pull-ups are great for strengthening the body, providing that you do them properly. If you ever have to climb a wall to escape a hungry horde of hooligans, you'll thank your lucky stars for all those pull-ups.

Some people like the idea of using weights to toughen their bodies. If you are going to use them, light weights are good enough for our purpose; they tone up the muscles but do not make them bulky. Fighters need lots of things but not big muscles – one look at any of the lighter boxing greats tells us that.

Yoga classes are marvellous for stretching the body and making it supple (see page 121). A good teacher will also show you how to relax your body when you have finished exercising, so that it can rest and refresh itself. A calm body leads to a calm mind, and suddenly life seems brighter and worries less important.

Of course fitness is only one cornerstone in the triangle of physical health: the other two are diet and sleep. Many of us do not sleep as well as we might, because we are unable to relax when we go to bed. And very few people eat a healthy, balanced diet. Our body engines run on what we feed them: rotten food and uneasy sleep make bad fuel.

Exercise can be great fun, and being fit and healthy feels great. But remember: moderation is the key. It's just as dangerous to strain the engine as it is to neglect it.

One day, your running ...

... jumping ...

... balancing ...

... and pull-ups may help you escape

5
THE SECRET WEAPON

This is the chapter of the Secret Weapon – a weapon so powerful and yet so readily available. It's there in each of us, just waiting to be used; it's the dividing line between the survivors and the rest.

We are the good guys: we don't like violence, and we hate anger and aggression. But sometimes we are going to find ourselves facing those who thrive on fear, sweat, blood and adrenalin – people to whom fighting is a way of life.

Walking along with a friend one evening, near Leicester Square, I noticed two men arguing with each other. One was a scruffy thin man with long wispy hair who was, rather surprisingly, wearing a suit and holding a briefcase in one hand. The other was broad and strong-looking, with a shaven head, wearing the skinhead uniform of T-shirt, jeans and heavy boots. He was about 5 foot 10 inches tall but immensely powerful. Suddenly he pushed the skinny man to the ground and started to kick him, but, as he did so, there came a roar and a rumbling from behind us. We turned to see a huge human lurching past. He was at least 6 foot 3 inches tall and massively built; not muscular, like the skinhead, but as heavy as an elephant. His head, arms, hands, thighs and stomach were all huge, and his long black greasy hair hung down to his shoulders, almost covering his eyes.

The skinhead looked up and noticed his new adversary coming to the rescue of the hapless businessman, who was feebly cringing on the ground. Losing interest in his original victim, the shaven thug turned to meet this more interesting challenge, while the business-man scrambled away into the safety of the night.

So there they stood, 5 feet apart: the monstrous stranger and the pure-beef hooligan, both ready for battle and roaring their jungle challenges into the night air like Godzilla and King Kong. All this had happened in seconds. My friend and I, realizing that extreme damage was about to be done to someone or something, ran to the nearest telephone box and phoned the police for help. We were away for about 3 minutes but on our return a new sight greeted us. Stretched out on the pavement lay the huge Godzilla, apparently lifeless, while astride his chest sat the victorious shaven King Kong. Holding his vanquished foe's hair in both hands, he was rhythmically smashing his head against the pavement.

The two of us threw caution to the winds and raced to the rescue. The plan was simple: run up, jump on to Kong's back, pull him off the fallen Godzilla, throw him to the ground and then – well, we weren't sure what to do then, but we would think of something. The first part of the plan went very well. We ran towards our target – King Kong's massive back – without a hitch and I reached it just ahead of my friend. As I opened my arms, spread my hands and prepared to jump, horror of horrors, the gorilla turned and saw me. The hands that had been playing basketball with Godzilla's head, stopped moving.

I saw a dim, primeval fire flickering in Kong's eyes, but, in a flash, my inspiration came. Like an actor in a Monty Python sketch, I suddenly fiddled with my fingers as though checking my nails and said, 'You'd better get away, the police are coming' – as if I had run up specially to tell him. Without a word, he leapt to his feet, turned and rushed past me, brushing my clothing as he went. No noise, no hesitation, just pure movement.

Now here's the frightening part: not only was this maniac young, fairly tall, immensely broad and strong, and unbelievably savage and violent, but he was also able to run with amazing speed. How intelligent he was, I'll never know, but that is the least of our worries. The only reason he didn't stop to annihilate both of us on his way home was that he knew there wasn't a minute to lose. He wasn't prepared to waste valuable time on mere underlings like us. His huge opponent lay defeated and bloodied, and his blood-lust was more than satisfied; it had been a good night and it was time to go.

Godzilla did not die that day. He actually got up and staggered back to his jungle lair somewhere in darkest Soho when nobody was looking. Kong, too, escaped the police and is still, presumably, stalking the streets looking for more victims. One day we may meet that villain, or the many like him, and have to fight for our very lives. We shall have to match his fighting spirit, and not let our fear overwhelm us before the first blow is struck. He would be a fearsome opponent. Only 5 foot 10 inches tall, he had faced a huge man and roared at him, answering his challenge. Then, like lightning, he had dived in with fists flailing, thrown him to the ground, jumped straight on top of him and finished the fight by virtually knocking his brains out. How can we deal with someone like this? How can we hope to face him without turning to jelly at the thought of what he wants to do to us? It's not easy, but with a bit of effort, it can be done. That is what this chapter is all about.

The happiest humans seem to be those who believe in themselves, who have confidence in their ability to deal with problems and hardship, and have faith in the resilience of their minds and bodies when the chips are down. That confidence becomes apparent in the tense seconds before a fight. Self-confidence is self-grown and, not being an expert on its cultivation, I'm not going to write about it. But I did mention in Chapter 2 that our body language – the way we walk and look around – reflects how we feel about ourselves. Therefore if we carry ourselves with pride, our self-esteem increases and others will notice.

If someone does come looking for trouble, he or she will pick a victim who does not look capable of causing any real problem. We need to make it clear by the way we stand and hold a gaze, and by the way we speak, that we cannot be so easily dismissed. In fact we have to show that we are prepared, if necessary, to do whatever it takes to survive. I'm not talking about aggression, but about asserting ourselves – firmly and resolutely. We can still give our opponent the chance to back off, we can still use reason, but he or she must realize that the wrong person has been picked for breakfast. He may win, but at what price? Countless books and classes teach the art of asserting oneself and, if you want to know more, turn to page 120.

Dealing with Fear

Most of us have a major problem when faced by a very unpleasant character who is screaming like an animal or explaining how he is going to separate us from parts of our body. It is called fear – massive, overwhelming, paralytic fear that turns legs to jelly, hands to castanets, and hearts to pumping turbines. Everyone will agree that fear is a powerful emotion, but few people realize that it is a friend and not an enemy. In fact its function is to mobilize the body, to prepare us for action: to pump adrenalin into our blood for faster muscle movement, and quicken our heart-beat and breathing for greater stamina. Without fear, we would be at a disadvantage; but, because we fear 'Fear', it becomes our master and stops us doing the very thing for which it has prepared us.

Feeling fear is not a prelude to defeat – we must never believe that. When facing an opponent, it is essential to concentrate only on that man or woman and not on our fear. If a fight is inevitable and we cannot escape, it is irrelevant what he or she intends to do to us, or whether he or she looks capable of doing it. What is relevant is that we must overwhelm our opponent quickly and effectively. We must accept that injury is a real possibility but realize that we have no choice: we must fight and, to survive, we must win. We cannot afford to lose.

Take our skinhead from Leicester Square as an example: he was 5 foot 10 inches tall, well-built, heavily muscled, fast, and ready to stand and fight. Those are relevant facts. To say that his face was ferocious, that he was wearing heavy boots and screaming horrible threats does not help you beat him; it just makes you more frightened than you already are. I am not underestimating him because that would be a serious mistake, but the greater our fear the more difficult it is to view him with that clinical detachment so vital for survival.

This is what you must do: freeze your emotions by concentrating on putting your opponent on to the computer screen of your mind. Within seconds, your brain will analyse him or her – height, weight, build, reach, age, weaknesses and strengths. Your brain will process, collate and evaluate that information before ordering you into action with all the force, speed and power that you have.

Unfortunately, a built-in survival aid in our memories often makes life more difficult – it's called 'association'. Our minds naturally associate people, places and events with past experiences so that we can stereotype them and decide whether they are good or bad for us. For example, many people would classify nuns as holy and sincere, while Hell's Angels are dismissed as troublemakers, drug-takers and wild drunks. This tendency to associate – designed to warn us of impending danger – can in fact work against us. The sight of a fearsome bully, intent on picking a fight, may fill us with such terror when our imagination starts working that we have lost the battle before it has even begun. A tough looker is not necessarily a tough fighter, and we should not do him the favour of allowing his warpaint to add to our problems. See through his make-up and only transfer the relevant data on to your mental screen.

It's not easy to stay detached, so keep your fear at bay by transforming it into anger – not uncontrollable fury but angry determination. Get angry about this bully, this cheap punk, this yob who reckons that you are a soft option; this hooligan who scouts the streets for weaker victims, who wants to beat you senseless so that he can brag about it to his beer-swilling pals in the local pub. Fuel your determination with that anger; you are determined to win, to overwhelm, to make him feel fear. Transform that determination into movement, speed and power, until you see the uncertainty in his eyes and the panic in his face. Only when he has run away or been hurt and stopped, can you allow that determination, that anger, to drain away. In addition, a couple of deep breaths calms the nerves wonderfully when your adrenalin is flowing.

Visualizing your opponent as he really is, without his fearsome trappings, is not easy; and concentrating the mind, to allow you to visualize, is also an acquired skill; but both concentration and visualization are widely taught techniques which can be mastered with practice. Many yoga classes teach easy methods and you will find all sorts of books on the subject in any library (see page 120). Spend some time reading or, even better, join a class and then practise, practise, practise – just for a few minutes each day.

Coming to terms with the fear that we all feel when in danger is different from being fearless. Being fearless is like being immune to pain: it means we do things which others, in their right minds, would never consider. Being fearless is a serious disadvantage.

I had a friend who could be described as fearless. He wasn't brave or courageous – just totally unaware of fear in times of crisis. He used to work as a policeman and, on the few occasions when he was in extreme danger, automatically did whatever had to be done without any thought for his own safety. His mind would become totally clear and his reactions devoid of any hesitation. Afterwards, he would sit down, realize the risks he had taken and start to worry about what he had done!

I remember him telling me how he once broke up a fight outside a nightclub. The fight was between five men who were being watched by a screaming crowd of about 60 onlookers. With a casual message into his radio, he marched straight in, grabbed one of the fighters and forced his way through the crowd using his prisoner as a shield. With his back to a wall and his prisoner in front of him, he faced the crowd until help arrived. This all sounds like dashing stuff, but if his sheer audacity had not carried the day, he would have been unable to defend himself against so many. Even he didn't consider such deeds heroic (heroes are usually frightened men who rise to the occasion), but saw himself as just a reckless fool whose luck would one day run out.

On a purely practical note, once you have assessed your opponent, avoid looking at any particular part of him. If you focus your eyes on his nose or his fists, you won't be able to see what he is doing with the rest of his body. But if you just gaze at him in his entirety, without looking at anything in particular, you will see every move he makes, as he makes it. You must have noticed things out of the corner of your eye every day of your life – this is very similar, and the ability vanishes as soon as the eye focuses on one object.

Taking the Initiative

As soon as you decide to attack your opponent, you must seize the initiative and strike first. Your mind must be clear just before and as you attack. If you're too busy thinking about what to do next, you won't see what your opponent is doing and that spells trouble.

To be able to fight instinctively without consciously planning as you go, you must know how and where to kick, punch, elbow, knee etc. You must also have practised these moves in a variety of combinations, using a small punchbag as a target, until you can automatically use the right move at the right time and distance.

In a real fight you should move in fast with a fearsome yell and overwhelm him with blows before he can hit you. If he doesn't give up immediately, stay with him. Whatever you do, don't back off and lose your mental and physical momentum. Keep going forward,

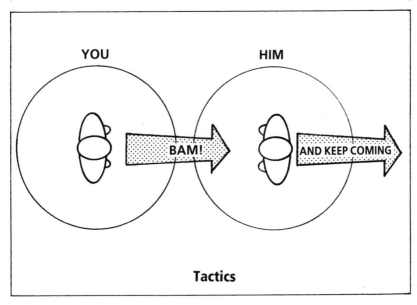

Tactics

atacking all the time; try to overwhelm him as quickly and finally as possible. You must break him psychologically – frighten him – before you can beat him physically. You may not be able to stick so close with a really big strong type whose one aim is to grab you and crush you, but you still don't have to back away. Move round him, piling on the pressure from different directions. Never give him the chance to recover.

Back in the days of the Wild West when it really was wild, the James gang – led by those notorious outlaws Jesse and Frank James – used the same approach when robbing banks. Galloping into town in their long prairie coats and dusty stetsons, with guns blazing and yelling like madmen, they would demoralize the opposition before they even reached the money. While some of the gang looted the safe, the rest of the gang would keep the streets clear with their fearsome yells, thundering hooves and deadly gunfire. Then, before you could say 'Lloyds-Barclays', they would vanish into the dust of the barren prairie.

You know where to find your secret weapon, but you will have to work hard to master it: learning how to befriend Fear, to visualize and detach, to channel anger into movement. Semi-contact sparring at a martial arts club is an excellent way of simulating the real thing. The Martial Arts Commission in London (see page 121) will advise you where to go.

The weapon is there – like the sword in the stone. Go and take it.

6
FIGHTING MOVES

If you have ever been cornered at a party by someone who insists on standing far too close for comfort while they lurch through their life history, you will know that around each of us there is a space which we like to call our own. When someone intrudes into that space, our natural reaction is to move back, unless they are a lover or an attacker, so that we can keep our private area intact. The daily sight of people squirming to avoid each other in a crowded tube train shows how uncomfortable we feel when our personal space is invaded.

Protecting Your Safety Zone

To protect ourselves from physical rather than social attack, we must extend that private area and, in times of danger, exclude from it anyone who is not a known friend. This larger area is a circle and we are at the centre of it. The radius of the circle is determined by the reach of our fists and feet, the weapons with which we can repel unwanted guests if necessary. Whenever a stranger approaches, we cannot allow him to enter our private area until we are sure he is safe and friendly, because, if he is not, he will easily be able to surprise us with a sudden attack.

You don't need to stand with your legs apart and fists clenched to enforce your safety zone; a well-balanced inoffensive stance is much more useful. It's quite simple to stay out of range of any possible attack without making it obvious to everyone in the street. For example, there is a right way and a wrong way of answering a stranger who has asked you for the time. The important point is that, while being helpful and polite, you must stay out of kicking or punching range, and you must make sure that the stranger is then

If you want to give the time ... don't
unnecessarily expose yourself to danger

Stay balanced, watchful and out of reach

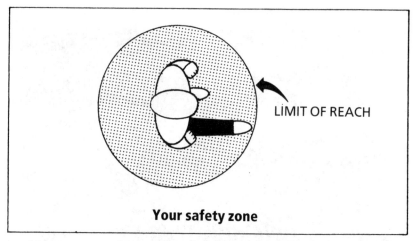

LIMIT OF REACH

Your safety zone

unable to narrow the gap between the two of you. Of course, if he looks dodgy then don't stop in the first place; just say that you don't carry a watch. This may all sound like an advanced case of paranoia but it's actually just a simple precaution which doesn't hurt anyone. Stopping people by asking for the time or change is a favourite mugging trick – especially when there is more than one attacker.

So how do you stop someone breaking into your personal area? Well, if they are obviously moving closer to attack you, then the moment they come within range, use all your available weapons against them. Your natural long-range weapons are your feet and hands; keep using them until the attacker backs off or lets you escape. So much for a blatant attack, but what about the friendly stranger who suddenly comes too close for comfort in the car park outside the local pub? You may lose some credibility with the clientele if you demolish him or her with a blitzkrieg attack only to find later that they had been looking for the nearest toilet!

This is what you can do: if he comes too close and narrows the gap, step to the side and extend it again; a gentle touch to his arm is more emphatic than asking him to stop. If he or she still insists on following you around, make it clear that they can come no closer. Using the fingers of your hand or even the heel of your palm, stop him or her moving towards you. Powered by your hips and shoulder, it is even quite easy to push a person off-balance in this way. Be careful not to leave your hand on their body for too long in case it is grabbed.

If all that doesn't stop the person, they are obviously looking for trouble of some sort and you must quickly decide whether to lash out first or run for safety. You can make your hand gestures more effective by adding a soundtrack: confidently telling an argumentative old drunk to sit down, as you gently push him back out of arm's reach, adds authority to the message. As I keep saying, our visual and verbal behaviour is one of our best bodyguards.

Talking can often get us out of sticky situations: talking sense to somebody, calming an explosive situation, giving the person a chance to back off without losing pride, or even pointing out the consequences or pointlessness of the whole exercise. I'll never forget the cellar of a little pub where I once stood for 10 agonizing minutes – (it seemed like a century) – with three of my friends, facing four of the meanest-looking characters I had ever met. I can remember their faces clearly to this very day. They were looking for trouble and they found us instead. We were the only ones in the cellar, apart from the barman who was too frightened to move an inch.

The only thing that stopped them cutting us to ribbons was that one of my friends had the gift of the gab and gradually defused the situation by talking good sense in a calm reasonable way; finally he pointed out that we would all end up in the local police cells if anything happened anyway. Right up until the four men left the cellar it was touch and go whether they would attack us. I remember their leader turning to go and wondering whether that was his signal for an all-out attack. Fortunately, the night was young and they were off to hunt elsewhere.

Bluff, like reason, can also work wonders, but be careful – one day someone may call it. As a 13-year-old child, I was sitting on a train when a middle-aged man came over and started talking. I didn't really understand what he was after but, although some of his questions sounded rather peculiar, I answered as best I could. He mumbled so badly that, half the time, I could only guess at what he might be saying. When I eventually realized that he was trying to chat me up, I decided to end the conversation and get off the train. At the next station, I told him I was leaving and, as he rose to follow me, I mentioned that my father was meeting me. He sat back down and we said goodbye. I watched the doors close and then ran upstairs to the empty ticket hall to wait for the next train.

Natural Weapons

Staying alert, being aware of what is going on, avoiding trouble and, if necessary, running for safety are all good techniques for self-preservation, but even the most careful person may one day have to fight to save himself, and to do that you need knowledge.

A tipsy stranger stumbles towards you

Turn to face him in a balanced stance

He comes too close, so step aside

A word of advice and a light hand gesture to keep him away

A firm push as he ignores you

He gets the message –
he is only being friendly

Soft Spots

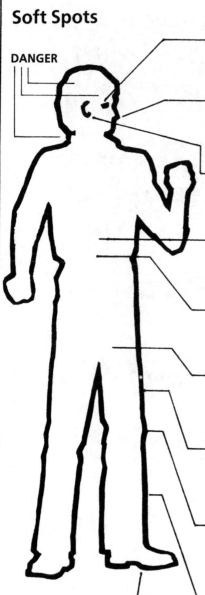

DANGER

Eyes:
A quick flick with the back of the fingers against his eyes will force him to blink, impairing his vision. (see Danger Note below).

Nose:
A very effective place to hit for three reasons: great pain, temporary loss of vision, but no lasting injury. At worst, you may break his nose (see Danger Note below).

Ear:
A sharp slap on one ear will send shock waves down the ear-canal, stunning your opponent (see Danger Note below).

Lower ribs:
These protect various organs like the liver and spleen which can be jolted and hurt when the lower ribs are struck.

Stomach/Belly:
Sensitive soft areas, so no risk of hurting yourself when you hit them. A good whack gives a bad ache and may even double up your opponent.

Groin:
The most famous target of all and consequently often the best defended. Any reasonable blow to the testicles hurts. Stomach ache is an additional side effect.

Thigh:
The schoolboy trick of giving someone a 'dead leg' – i.e. kneeing them in the side of the thigh – is very effective and causes great pain but usually no lasting injury.

Knee:
The knee is a complex joint and a hard kick to the front, side or back of it could produce permanent damage. It will certainly cause pain and slow him down.

Shin bone:
Unprotected by muscle, this can be a very painful area. A hard kick could even cause a fracture.

Arch of the Foot/Toes:
Can both be stamped on. Very vulnerable and easily broken, causing pain and loss of movement.

Natural Weapons

Knee:
A real battering ram; its only drawback is that your groin is vulnerable as you move in.

Ball of the foot:
The weapon with the longest range; very versatile and effective, especially when followed with hand or knee blows.

Heel:
Tremendously powerful; the entire force of your movement is concentrated into the small hard area of your shoe heel. A real crusher.

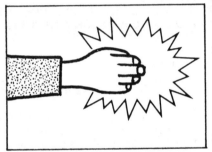

Open palm:
Has a stunning or stinging effect, although it is not as fast as a punch and is consequently easier to block or grab.

Punch:
Very fast but not so good for weaker fighters.

Heel of the palm:
Fast and less prone to injury than a punch.

Danger Note

Hitting some of the soft spots in certain ways can cause really serious injury and can only be justified in extreme circumstances. This is the type of damage that you could innocently cause:

Ear:
Simultaneously slapping both ears with cupped hands can cause permanent deafness. In any case, you yourself are very vulnerable as you get ready to strike.

Eyes:
Poking the eyes, as opposed to just flicking them, can blind your opponent for life. Can you justify that?

Nose:
An upward blow to the nose, driving it towards the forehead, could seriously injure your attacker when you only intended to give him a bloody nose.

Skull/Temple:
A strong blow to a weak part of the skull, such as the temple, could cause brain damage, leading to coma and even death.

Neck/Throat:
Hitting the throat can cause death by asphyxiation, hemorrhage or blood clotting. Striking the side or back of the neck can damage the spine or the spinal cord itself, sometimes permanently.

You need to know where to find your enemy's weak spots, how to hit them effectively, and which parts of your own body to use. As you can see from the first diagram, the body of even the toughest fighter is covered with 'soft spots' (or vulnerable areas) which can easily be seen and reached. The second diagram shows the natural weapons which everyone carries. Put the two together and decide the best ways to attack each one of those sensitive points; then turn to page 77 and compare your answers. Ultimately, this may be the only way to beat the baddies – to hurt them until they leave well alone. No matter how unpleasant it is to damage another human being, fighting is sometimes still a vital part of self-preservation.

When using your hands, feet and knees to attack your opponent, make sure that you start from a balanced position. You should be relaxed until the actual point of impact when, with a great shout, you tense your body and deliver every ounce of strength via your hand or foot. If your body is tense before you hit home, you will only

Knee: Protect your groin and throat, yell, and thrust your hip forward for extra power.
Grabbing your opponent increases the effect of the blow

The fist: turn your hips and shoulders first
Then lash out with your fist and yell

Make sure that your wrist
is in the right position ...

... if it's not, you may break it

As your left hand comes back, follow with
the right, turning your hips and shoulders
the other way

Punch and yell. Remember to protect your
throat at all times

Heel of the palm: same movement as the
punch. Once again, protect yourself and yell

Open palm (slapping): the same movement
as the punch but use a whipping motion as
you hit. Protect your throat and yell

slow yourself down. Concentrate on smooth, fast movement before you start worrying about power – that will come with practice. The yell, as you connect, automatically tenses your body by forcing you to breathe out, and that tension increases the impact on your chosen soft spot.

Some people prefer to yell at the start of their movement to frighten their opponent and increase their own confidence. They still

Ball of the foot: lift your thigh until it is almost parallel with the ground. Protect your face and turn up the toes of your kicking foot. Your supporting leg should be slightly bent for better balance

Thrust your hips forward
for greater power as
you kick, and yell

Either step back (you
may have missed or
decide to run) or ...

breathe out when they strike, forcing the air out of their body and tensing their muscles. The martial arts call this 'focusing your blow' and it really makes all the difference. That, along with the kicks and punches shown, has to be practised, and there is no better place to do it than in a kick-boxing or Thai boxing class. These rely on actual physical contact. If that's not your cup of tea, choose a karate or boxing club to learn the basic movements (see page 121).

Step forward and ...

follow up with a punch or ...

your knee

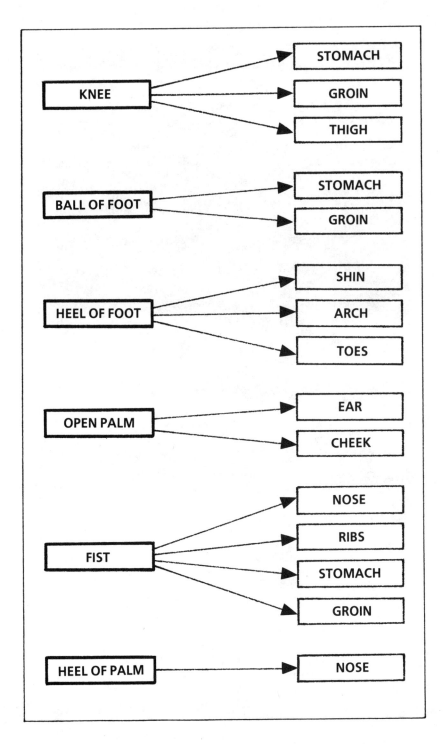

The heel of the foot (a good move if you've
been grabbed): lift your foot and look for
your target

Stamp down hard with
your heel. Don't forget to
yell as you do it

The same movement,
but forwards

Apart from focusing your blow, you also have to be able to judge your distance, so that if you ever have to kick or punch somebody, you'll automatically know whether you can reach them. Any solid target, whether it's a small punchbag or a cardboard box suspended from the ceilling by string, is fine for this. Remember, you are practising distance, not power.

Speed, as I said in Chapter 5, is absolutely vital. When you move in, you must move in fast – really fast. In fact in self-defence everything should be done fast. You must be quick to notice things around you; you must decide in an instant whether to run or fight; you must practise turning at speed to defend yourself against attacks from the side and behind. It sounds obvious, but some people are really not used to moving fast.

If you can simulate attacking and being attacked, then you are far more likely to find out whether your tactics and movements are effective. Practising with a partner can be dangerous and requires good communication, discipline and supervision as even friends can get over-excited during training and injuries are always possible. Supervision is available at many martial arts clubs which, depending on their art, provide a broad spectrum of experience – from the fairly realistic to the actual thing.

Like everything else, you must practise until these moves become automatic. When it comes to the crunch, you won't have time to start thinking about what to do next. Only thoughts, actions, moves and attacks which have been practised until they are second nature will be available at a split second's notice.

Surprise

Physical muscle is not the only weapon in your armoury. A surprise attack is a superb card to have up your sleeve, especially when you combine it with a mind-numbing yell and a distracting dummy movement. You don't have to stand in a classic karate or boxing stance to kick or punch someone. As before, the stance is well-balanced and the groin, ribs and stomach are slightly protected by the posture of the body and the front arm. Totally relaxed, with hands open, there is no hint of an imminent lightning attack.

Deciding that he must strike first to save himself, our hero launches into a well-practised routine. With a deep roar, he raises his right hand to distract his opponent while his left hand is already starting to lash out, smooth and relaxed. As it crashes into its target, our hero breathes out sharply, tensing his whole body and sending shock waves shuddering through his clenched fist. Quickly drawing back his hand, he must decide in a split second whether to run, or physically beat his opponent.

One word of warning: don't assume that your surprise attack is always going to work, otherwise you might get a nasty surprise yourself. At school, I once had an argument with a boy from another form and we decided to meet in the break to settle it with our fists. Realizing that he was the better fighter, I decided to gain the upper hand by launching a surprise attack. We both turned up with our seconds and, taking off our jackets, walked towards each other to discuss the rules of engagement. As I started to speak to him, I suddenly brought my knee up, as hard as possible, into his crutch. My hands, face and body didn't give my intentions away and the move was quick enough to catch him completely off-guard. I stood there waiting for him to fall over but unfortunately nothing happened. He just looked at me and then punched me straight in the face. We both went crashing over and a furious fight ensued until two big prefects dragged us apart.

Realizing that my opponent and I were safely separated, I struggled violently, hurling threats and abuse at the poor boy, while praying that my large saviour wouldn't let go of me. Whether my knee found its target, I don't know. What is important is that I was so surprised by my opponent's failure to fall over in agony that I was unable to stop him attacking me. Apart from that one pitfall, surprise attacks are an excellent tactic and should be used whenever possible.

Even a simple surprise attack takes practice. The punch must be fluid and accurate, the stance must be relaxed and the yell must be deep from the stomach, not high-pitched from the back of the throat. As for the dummy, you must be ready to strike as you do it, because the distracting effect on your opponent is short-lived. It's no good dummying and then getting ready to punch somebody; the two must be almost simultaneous.

Back in ancient China, the various martial arts schools were bitter rivals; such rivals, in fact, that their students used to compare fighting skills, sometimes to the death. One school suddenly lost some of its best students over a period of a few weeks. All were found dead, stabbed in the stomach, presumably killed by rival fighters from the school down the road. The duels between these two groups were fought with knives which they carried in small scabbards on their belts, and it was only some time later that the rival school's knockout tactics were discovered. The trick was

A relaxed but balanced
stance. Don't let your
hands, face or body
give your intentions away

Dummy, yell
and raise your fist

Bam!

wearing the knife in the scabbard upside-down on the belt. When his unlucky opponent approached, the fighter would grab the scabbard with his right hand and raise it in the air as if it were the knife. While the duped adversary prepared to defend himself against the apparently raised weapon, the student's left hand would draw the upside-down dagger from his belt and plunge it into his rival's stomach. Sneaky, but very effective.

So now you have three weapons when standing face to face with someone who wants to hurt you: physical power, surprise and deception. When combined, they make you a force to be avoided.

Defence Against an Unarmed Attacker

Not every fight starts with two people standing watching each other. Someone may jump onto you or grab you in a lonely street. Or, during a fight, your opponent may try to strangle or crush you, rather than hit out with his or her hands and feet. There are many ways to grab a person but they are all to be avoided for two reasons. First, every time you grab somebody with your hands or arms, you lose the use of those natural weapons, because you can't use them to hit out or to defend yourself. Second, to be able to grab your opponent, you have to come in close. And once in range, without hands to protect yourself, you are extremely vulnerable. We don't need to grab people in self-defence: the police restrain prisoners and killers strangle victims, but we don't fit into either category. Still, people often do it without thinking, especially in a fight when everyone falls over and starts rolling about on the ground.

There are hundreds of ways of escaping from all the different grabs, holds and strangles. As I said, whoever has grabbed you is extremely vulnerable. He or she is well within range and unable to defend him or herself with one or both hands. What you must do is lash out with all your available natural weapons until the shock and pain of your attack forces them to let go.

If your legs are being held, use your hands; if the person has grabbed your wrists, bash him or her with your head, knees and feet; and so on. Whatever they are not holding, should be hitting back mercilessly. You can stamp on toes, feet or shins; knee him in the thigh or groin; grab and squeeze testicles or pinch the soft inside of thighs along the trouser seam; elbow him or her in the ribs or stomach if the person is behind you, or knee them in the belly if in front; grab the little finger of one of the hands that is holding you round the waist or arms, and bend it backwards, forcing him or her to let go; bite the side of the neck or slap a cheek or ear; bash the nose with the front or back of your head; force the head back by pressing your fingers up nostrils or squeezing the flats of your thumbs into eyes; or even spit into eyes to make them blink.

Wherever you are grabbed, you cannot be stopped using at least some of these weapons, and every time one hits home, the attacker's pain will increase until he or she is forced to loosen the grip. When that happens, you must bash hard and then run like the wind.

There are two dangers which need a special mention: one is strangling. You can be strangled from the front or behind, by one hand, two hands or the arms; if properly strangled, you will pass out in a matter of seconds. Don't bother to struggle against the hands or arms that are holding your throat; they will be strong. What you must do is tense your neck muscles to relieve the pressure and then hurt your attacker so quickly and painfully that he will loosen his grip, allowing you to move and gasp for air – before you smash him and run. Time is vital whenever your breathing is involved.

The second threat is the man or woman who grabs you, not to restrain or crush you, but to keep you still while they hit you. Someone may grab your collar with both hands in order to head-butt you in the face, or may seize you by the hair to punch you. Whatever you do, make sure you avoid that head or fist – just moving your body or face slightly to the side will often be enough, providing you don't pull against their grip. That's what they expect, so move with it. Ignore the fact that they are holding you, and hit them first and fast. Leave the hands on your collar but slam your fist or elbow into the attacker's nose. Forget the hand on your hair even though it hurts, and ram the heel of your palm into his mouth as he raises his own fist. Once you have stopped the attacker in his tracks, then you can deal with the grip itself, but until then it is a second priority.

Such drastic tactics are of course only justifiable against a violent attack. Someone who has grabbed your wrist as an unfunny joke only deserves, if reason fails, a sharp slap round the face.

It's a good idea to find yourself a partner and practise all these close-in moves. Get used to being grabbed and reacting quickly. One word of warning: although you should learn to resist strangling by tensing your neck muscles and hitting out hard, it is an extremely dangerous exercise even between friends. *Only* practise this under skilled supervision. A judo class (see page 121) is the perfect place: the teacher can come to your aid and even resuscitate you if things go wrong. Whenever practising any release with a partner, have a prearranged signal for stopping and letting go, like the double hand tap on the attacker's arm which is used in judo. The moment your opponent feels these taps he or she must let go immediately. Never have a spoken signal; you can't speak when you are being throttled and, by the time that your partner has realized that you are in difficulty, it may be too late to revive you.

As I said before, people do fall over during fights. If you're unlucky, you will be the only one to end up on the ground. The British commandos in the Second World War didn't bother to teach their men how to defend themselves on the ground because they felt that, even in an unarmed fight, the chances of survival were minimal once anybody went down. I don't agree; as with everything else in this book, a couple of simple rules can help immensely.

The first thing to do is get up as quickly as possible, so practise falling down in all directions and jumping up again as fast as you can – until the whole movement becomes automatic. Sometimes this will not be possible. You may hurt yourself when you hit the ground, or your opponent may be so close that he or she can hit you immediately. You must keep the attacker at bay with your legs – one leg out ready to kick him with the heel, the other held slightly back out of reach to protect your groin.

If the attacker tries to run round your legs, swivel round on your back and buttocks with your arms out on the ground at right angles to your body. (Practise that defensive movement with a friend and you will be amazed at how fast you can turn to protect yourself, and how difficult you can make it for him or her to hit you.) If the attacker comes within range of your heel, kick a knee or shin, but make sure that you don't let them grab your feet. Throw earth and stones at their face, then jump up and hit them. The longer you stay on the ground, the lower your chances of escape.

Even if he gets round your leg guard and starts kicking you, keep going. Protect your body with your feet and forearms; roll into his legs and smother his kicks, then pull him down and start unleashing all those close-in weapons mentioned earlier. Jump up quickly whenever you can and either keep fighting or escape. These may be simple moves, but they increase your chances of surviving the day intact – maybe with a few bruises, cuts and even broken bits, but still intact.

Those of you who are keen to learn how to fall over without hurting yourself (usually) should again find a good judo class (see page 121). If you don't have the time or inclination, remember one thing: when you fall or are pushed onto your back, front or side, always keep your head raised as you hit the ground. One good bash on the head and you're finished before you've even started, so falling with your head raised is worth practising as well.

Defence Against an Armed Attacker

Sometimes bare hands and feet are not enough. Even a skilled fighter would be unlikely to beat off an armed attacker without suffering some sort of injury. When I say 'armed', I'm talking about the usual street weapons: knives, machetes, razors, chains, bottles and sticks – not guns. Should anybody point a gun at you, just *do what he says*. You should only consider doing anything else if you are absolutely certain that he is definitely going to kill you, in which case you don't have much to lose. Guns fired at close range do, unlike television cop shows, blow holes in people. One bullet in the wrong place can cripple you for life or send your blood gushing on to the pavement.

One day, minding my own business as usual, I was walking down a busy main road in the afternoon when I saw a helmeted security guard standing outside a doorway. Instead of keeping watch on the street, he was giving directions to a young woman tourist. A tiny alarm bell rang at the back of my head: could this be the classic distraction trick that comes just before a robbery? As I passed the two of them a second security guard came out of the doorway, holding a fat canvas money-bag. Suddenly a young man wearing a full-face motorcycle helmet rushed up behind me and stuck a revolver in the security guard's face. He screamed some incoherent threat, and I honestly looked round to check that I wasn't on a film set. It only took half a second to realize that I was not on camera but had strolled into a genuine 'stick-up'. Waving the gun around, the young man snatched the bag, turned and ran.

I couldn't see whether the revolver was a replica or real, and I certainly wasn't going to risk my life for what could have been a bag of pennies. As the robber ran into and along the road, I followed at a distance of about 10 yards, keeping to the pavement so that the line of parked cars stood between us. Suddenly he dashed across the street, dodging the traffic, and jumped on to a small motorbike. As I followed him across the road, he roared off – straight through green traffic lights and into the distance. I had got what I wanted – his registration number and, in no time at all, the police were all over the place. I doubt whether they caught him because no one ever asked me to make a statement or come to court; but then you never

Fall with your head raised

Keep him at bay with your feet

Go for his legs when you can

know, he may have pleaded guilty. The point of the story is that no one can take risks when there are guns around. You don't get a second chance – fatal wounds stay fatal.

Another weapon commanding the highest respect is the knife, or any form of knife like a machete, razor or flick-knife. Some knives have sharp edges for slashing, others have points for stabbing, and some can do both. All are absolutely lethal. Countless self-defence books show how to grab the arm of the attacker and force him to drop his knife. That's fine in theory, but in reality we have a problem. Bearing in mind that the knife is a lethal weapon, what happens if you get it wrong? What happens if, as you move in close to grab his arm, he suddenly kicks you hard in the groin, and then stabs you as you double over in agony? You cannot afford to be within range of the knife; one stab in the wrong place and it's all over.

If the average person fought any reasonably competent knifeman with bare hands, it's unlikely that he or she would survive a determined effort to stab them to death. Even a trained fighter would be in trouble. I used to know a policeman, a young and intelligent man, who trained in the French fighting system of Savate. His beat was in North London. One night he was walking down a narrow, dark lane when suddenly, from behind a parked van, a huge man appeared. He was about 6 foot tall and well-built. In his right hand he carried a long machete, but it was the crazed look in his eyes that really shook the young policeman. He had no time to call for help on his radio because, even as he saw him, the man rushed forward, the machete held high above his head. The constable spent the next 10 minutes fighting for his life. He fought with everything he had – his helmet, his raincoat, his truncheon, his kicks, rubble from the ground; he even used the van to shield himself from the frenzied attack which relentlessly beat him back. Then, just as suddenly as he had appeared, the man turned and ran off. The policeman radioed for help but the machete man was never found.

Who knows why he attacked the young constable? One thing was clear: he had certainly meant to kill him, and had only been stopped by the officer's determined and intelligent fighting. His victim had been lucky, escaping with only minor wounds. Would the average person, who never thinks about such things and is unfit and unsteady, have survived? I doubt it.

The policeman only stood and fought because he couldn't run; and run is what you must always do whenever knives come out. Unlike guns, they are unlikely to hit you as you run away. There is a tremendous myth about throwing knives – very few people can do it properly and it is extremely difficult to hit a moving target. So, whenever you can, run. If you can't run, use reason to dissuade your

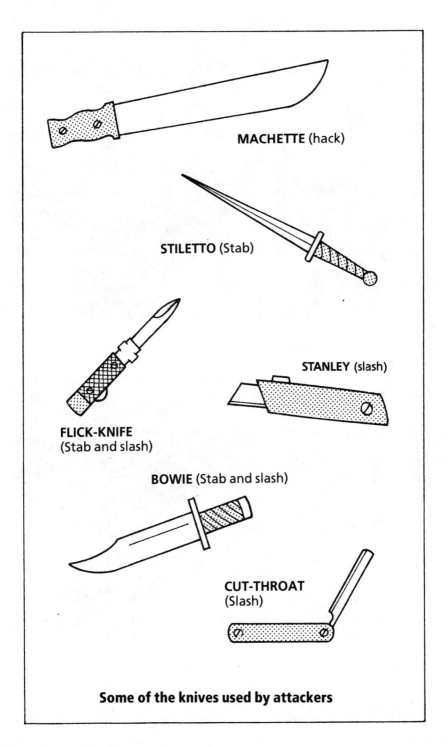

MACHETTE (hack)

STILETTO (Stab)

STANLEY (slash)

FLICK-KNIFE
(Stab and slash)

BOWIE (Stab and slash)

CUT-THROAT
(Slash)

Some of the knives used by attackers

His raised knife may be a diversion for

... a side stab ...

... or a kick

attacker, but if reason fails you will have to stand and fight.

To even the odds, use anything that comes to hand. The longer the weapon you find, the greater your range and the bigger your protection zone. Take a walk around the streets one day and have a look at all the innocent objects lying about which you could use to defend yourself in a desperate situation. Here are a few ideas: pick up anything that could be used as a baton, not too short and not too long – a piece of wood, a length of metal, a strong branch, a short piece of scaffolding or part of a wooden fence would do. Use it as a truncheon if it is fairly short, smashing at a hand or any part of a body that comes within range as it moves towards you. Don't let an attacker back you into a corner; move round and keep your safety zone intact.

If your weapon is long enough, use it like a bayonet, jabbing it

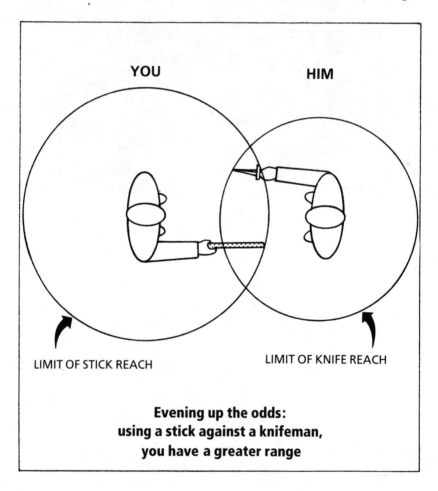

YOU   **HIM**

LIMIT OF STICK REACH   LIMIT OF KNIFE REACH

**Evening up the odds:
using a stick against a knifeman,
you have a greater range**

with both hands, aiming at eyes and throat and forcing the attacker to back off; an umbrella is excellent for this. These are drastic actions, and they need to be; this person is about to carve you up or even murder you. The only way to stop them is to get in first or persuade them that it's a big mistake; either way you have to fight.

Look around for anything which can serve as a shield, like a dustbin lid. Or, even better, find a shield which can also be used as a ram (like a chair, stool, dustbin or small table) to knock the knifeman down or against a wall. Throw anything that you can lay your hands on: heavy stones to send the attacker running for cover; earth, grit, coins from your pocket or even hot coffee to throw in the eyes. Finally, grab yourself a makeshift whip: lash out at the face with the leather belt from your waist so that it cracks like the real thing. Or use a flexible tree branch or heavy jacket as a flail to beat the person back. If, by a stroke of luck, the knife is dropped, don't make yourself vulnerable by bending down to pick it up; jump in and kick it out of reach.

Broken bottles are just as dangerous as knives and should be treated with equal respect. Sticks and chains, although sometimes lethal, are slightly easier to deal with, because unlike the knife and bottle, which are lethal at any distance, they are less adaptable. Sticks can be stabbed at you but chains cannot; they must be swung, and the heavier they are, the slower the swing – giving you more time to get out of the way. Although short sticks can be used to jab at close range, longer sticks and chains become almost useless when there is no room to swing them in, or against a very close opponent. All these weapons can be lethal and the same tactics must be used against each one: stay out of range of the weapon; grab anything that equals the odds and extends your own striking range; and fight back with such determination and intensity that your attacker is either overwhelmed or forced back, allowing you to escape.

A stab wound or knife cut can easily be fatal, and it's really worth knowing how to treat them. Whether you save yourself, a wounded friend or even an unconscious attacker, the knowledge is vital. So few people know first aid (for some strange reason it's not taught in most schools) that you may be the only one who can plug the wound and stop the bleeding. The St John Ambulance publishes an excellent first aid book (see page 120) which is interesting, straightforward, well-illustrated and cheap. I advise you to buy it – it may come in handy one day.

An umbrella can be used ...

as a bayonet

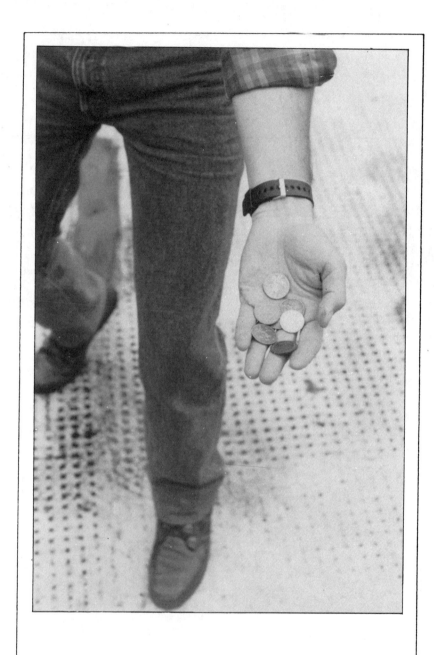

Coins to block his vision

A magazine as a truncheon (bash or jab)

A chair as a shield with prongs

A belt as a whip

Using the Space Around You

Whoever you are fighting, whether they are armed or not, it is always important to make the best use of the space around you. There is usually a better and a worse spot to stand and fight. Run to a position where your attacker has to struggle upwards to reach you, like a staircase. If more than one person is attacking you, fight with your back to a wall (not a low wall in case you trip over it) so that no one can come round behind you. Or fight from a place where they can only reach you one at a time, like a doorway or narrow staircase. Avoid being boxed into a corner, and always fight with a strong sun behind you.

Like the constable in the story, use any cover to keep your attacker at bay: cars, pillars, and tables all fit the bill. Let's say you are in a room with a big table in the middle of it; and your attacker is standing near the only exit. The table is too heavy to move, so you can't ram him into the wall with it, and there are no other weapons around. If he's on his own, and not waiting for his friends to come in and help him, sooner or later he has to come and get you. By keeping the table between the two of you, you could lure him round it so that you end up nearer the exit; the same idea can be used in the street with parked cars. Of course, once you have outwitted him, you must be fast on your feet.

Escaping

Running for safety is the best way to escape trouble. In any dodgy situation, whether you are walking down a lonely street or standing in a crowded bar where an argument is brewing, make sure that you are aware of possible escape routes. If someone does pick on you and you can't escape without fighting, have the courage to accept that trouble is inevitable, the foresight to check that your escape route is clear, and the resolve to attack first. An escape route may be a back door, a side road or a low wall fronting a garden. It's an alternative path to safety so that, when the obvious path is blocked, you can still get away.

If you manage to break free from your attacker, run to the nearest source of help, whether it's a house with lights on, an open garage, pub or shop, or a police or fire station– any place where you can find people, a telephone, weapons or cover.

Just in case you are thinking of shouting 'Help' as you run down

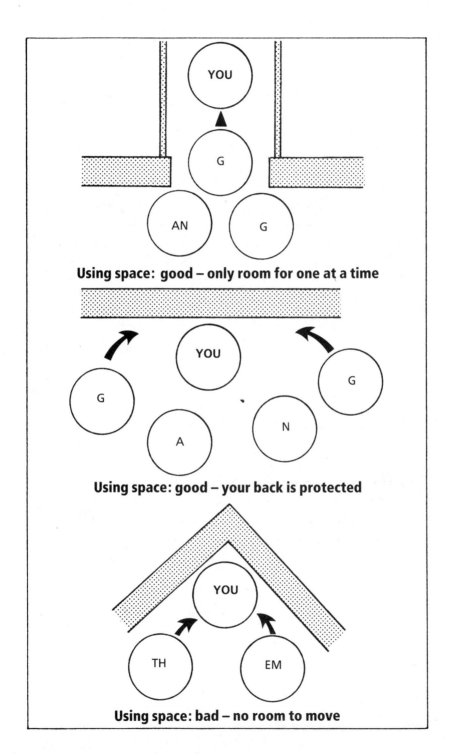

Using space: good – only room for one at a time

Using space: good – your back is protected

Using space: bad – no room to move

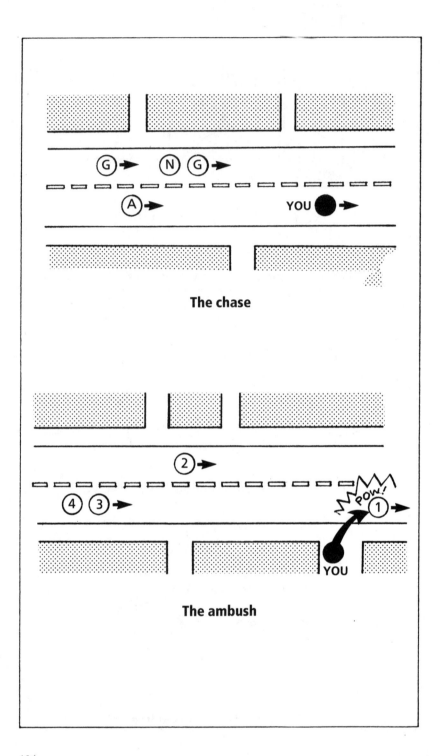

The chase

The ambush

the street, don't expect immediate results. Most people, when they hear screaming, either think it is a gang of yobs or quarrelling lovers. Let me tell you a story: a prostitute was attacked by a young man in the back yard of a large block of flats in London. She fought him tooth and nail for a good 20 minutes, screaming at the top of her voice, until he eventually beat her senseless and killed her. Not only did no one come to her aid or telephone the police, but residents actually closed their windows so that they wouldn't be disturbed. When the police turned up, they couldn't find a single witness – no one wanted to know.

A more effective cry is 'Fire' because everyone sticks their heads out in case it is their house or car that is about to be burnt down. Once people see that you are in trouble, then they may help you.

Back in Chapter 4, I mentioned that pull-ups were very useful exercises because they strengthen the muscles needed to pull yourself up over a high wall. It's also worth learning how to jump from a height so that you can get down again on the other side. Reduce the distance to the ground by hanging from the wall, look down to your landing space, and as you drop, push yourself away to avoid bashing into the wall. Land with your legs together, knees bent, on the balls of your feet, with your forearms protecting your head, and roll on to your side just like a paratrooper does. Get up as fast as possible. Quickly look around to make sure that you haven't jumped out of the frying pan into the fire and, if all is well, start running.

If help is nowhere to be found, and you can't outrun whoever is chasing you, then substitute cunning for speed. Two rival regiments of the peacetime British Army found themselves quartered in the same town. Of course there were the usual fights, but one regiment soon found that its men were generally taking more punishment than they were giving out. The other side's tactics were simple: whenever outnumbered, they would run for safety, picking up whatever weapons came to hand as they went. Running until their pursuers had become separated by the chase, they would turn and ambush them one after the other. Not exactly the Queensberry Rules, but it worked.

We can do exactly the same: look around for good ambush spots as you run, places which give you cover so that you can jump out and completely surprise your attacker as he rushes past. If the situation is desperate, pick up any makeshift weapon you can find, and use it. One point to remember: when several people are chasing you, make sure that they have, in fact, become separated before you jump out and ambush the nearest pursuer. Otherwise you may get a nasty shock.

Look down the wall to your landing space

Push away from the wall as you jump

Land properly and ...

roll over to absorb the shock

Get up fast, look around, and move on

Hiding

Unfortunately ambush isn't always possible. There may not be any suitable places to use, or your attackers may all be equally fit and able to stick together while they chase you. With no help around, you may have to resort to another tactic – a risky one: going to ground. Hiding is fine provided you are sure that the chances of discovery are absolutely minimal. If the gang does track you down to your hiding place, you are definitely out of luck.

Here are a few guidelines: don't hide in obvious places – like behind dustbins in a dead-end alley or behind a fallen tree trunk in an open meadow. If you are not completely covered, hide where you blend into your surroundings so that your outline or the colour and texture of your clothes, hair and skin don't give you away. Make sure that you don't leave any footprints or other traces of movement on the way to your hiding place. And, once you're there, stay absolutely quiet – take slow, calm, soft breaths and don't move an inch until you are sure that the coast is clear. After all that, remember one thing: the faster you can run, the more likely you are to escape.

This has been a fairly gritty chapter, all about beating up baddies, causing them pain and putting them to flight. Sometimes it has to be done but, even then, two things separate us from our attackers. First, we never fight unless we have to; and second, even when we do fight, we stop as soon as the threat to our health and safety has been removed. If we forget these differences, then we are no better than the bullies who figure so prominently in this book.

7

WHO ARE THE
BADDIES?

This book is all about defending yourself against baddies but, so far, I haven't mentioned much about the specific types of this particularly unpleasant breed. Well, the same principle applies to each of them: take the initiative and keep it – whether avoiding, escaping, deterring or fighting them. You must always be the one who decides what to do and when. Extending this principle a little further, each one of these types expects a certain reaction from their chosen victim – perhaps terror, disgust, humiliation or just stunned silence. So don't give it to them. Instead, give them the reaction you've chosen. Give them a nasty shock; a surprise which is going to put you one step ahead before things have even started. This chapter tells you how to do it.

Muggers

Muggers are becoming increasingly vicious – some even slash their victims before they ask for the money. They have to be taken seriously, because so many carry weapons which they are prepared to use, as the next story shows. An elderly British couple, on holiday in the South of France, were standing near their car on a deserted country road when a stranger approached them. Gesturing towards the car with the axe in his hand, he demanded the keys from the husband who flatly refused to co-operate. Without a word, the stranger buried his axe in the man's head, killing him instantly. He calmly picked up the fallen keys, climbed into the car and drove away, leaving the widow staring at her dead husband.

Muggers aim to terrify their victims so that they can't react rationally. It's difficult to think about things for the first time in the heat of the moment, so plan it out now. For your own safety, give the mugger what he wants. Make it clear that you intend to co-operate, but do it your way. Instead of handing your valuables or bag to him or her, drop them on the ground between you. That way, you stay out of range and test the mugger's true intentions: if he ignores your offering and continues towards you, then you, and not the money are the target. Don't do it in a provocative way – just quickly and calmly step back a couple of paces when you have finished, to increase the distance between you. If he or she asks you to pick something up, assert yourself or defuse the situation but don't bend down. Keep well back!

What you do next is up to you. If you are sure that the mugger has no intention of attacking you, you may decide to stay until he or she grabs the loot and runs off; or you may decide to turn and run as they bend down – either to safety or to the nearest available weapon. If you are convinced that he or she is going to hurt you and you can't escape, you may even hit out as they come forward. Think carefully about each option so that, if the worst comes to the worst, you will be prepared.

As for the muggers who injure first and rob later, there is only one thing you can do: keep your eyes open, be aware of people around you, know what they are doing and look for likely ambush spots. With a little practice, such awareness becomes second nature.

Gangs

Gangs may fight their rivals for the sake of supremacy and pride, but they only attack innocent strangers for fun. They are not looking for a tough fight but for a victim – someone who will cower or quake with fear like a doomed rabbit.

So take the initiative: if you can't avoid them, outrun them or reason with them, you are going to have to fight your way out. Make no mistake, the odds are stacked against you, but you still have a chance if you play your cards right. Unless they catch you unawares and rush you immediately, the gang will try to surround or corner you, so make sure that your back is against something and avoid corners. They will expect you to watch helplessly as their trap gradually tightens, so don't wait – break through their line as quickly as possible and run to find help, weapons or a better place to stand and fight.

Grab any makeshift weapon as the gang approaches – something which can be used as a club or baton is best – and attack at once. Don't let them close in; the wider apart they are, the better your

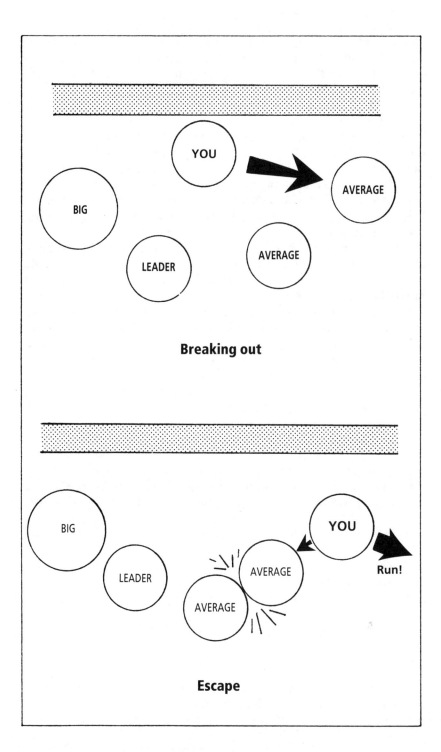

Breaking out

Escape

chances of escape – especially when armed with a club. Wade through them, swinging it from left to right in a figure of eight and yelling like mad, forcing them back as you break out towards safety like a samurai in the Tokyo rush hour.

Once they manage to get close, you really are in trouble. Let's say you are backed against a wall, facing four football supporters who have sneaked up and surprised you and now intend to enjoy themselves. The two men on the left are both about 5 foot 9 inches tall and reasonably built; the two on the right are much bigger and one of them – the one in the middle – is the leader of the gang.

If there were only two men, the best tactic would be to flatten the leader with a surprise attack, before turning on his demoralized friend, assuming that you had the power and speed to do that. As there are four men surrounding you in a close semicircle, you must aim for their weak point – the smaller of the two end men. Your only hope is to use him as a shield against the rest of the gang as you break through their line.

With a resounding yell, dummy to your right with your hands while you launch yourself at your target – the man on your far left. Finish him with one hard accurate kick to the groin and immediately push him into the rest of the pack as you run like the wind. To pull this off, you need to be fast, powerful and accurate, and that means lots of practice in your back garden. Even then, once surrounded, your chances of escaping are not high, but you have absolutely nothing to lose.

As an alternative to a good kicking, the gang may decide to have some fun once they have rushed you. One or two of them may grab your arms while a third gets ready to hit you from the front. Although you are in a seemingly hopeless situation, keep thinking and get your priorities right. Forget the two behind you; your target is the one who is about to start lashing out. Once you have smashed your foot into his groin and changed his mind, you can deal with the others. It's a long shot, but well worth trying.

Football supporters aren't the only ones who go around *en masse.* Girls and women also prey in groups and are equally dangerous. So keep your eyes open and your outlook broad.

Bullies

At school I was fairly skinny and not big for my age. That, on its own, was no problem, but I also had the misfortune to fall foul of one of the school bullies. He used to make my life very uncomfortable –

abusing me and pushing me around – but I never had the guts to hit him because he was so big.

One day he came up behind me and pushed me into a metal locker. Not only did he give me a shock, he also hurt me. I was suddenly filled with great anger and, without thinking, I turned round and delivered the most beautiful right hook to his jaw as he stood there grinning. He staggered back a few steps and, massaging his face, mumbled in complete astonishment to nobody in particular: 'He hit me!'

He was not the only one who was surprised – I was absolutely amazed! So much so that I was totally unable to move. Luckily, I had a speech up my sleeve prepared for just such a glorious occasion. I firmly told him that if he ever came near me again, I would fight back for all I was worth and, even if he managed to beat me every time, sooner or later I would get lucky and hurt him. He never troubled me again – in fact, he even used to say good morning to me on the way to school.

Like gangs, bullies are not looking for a stand-up fight, but for a victim; the best way to beat them is to give more trouble than they can handle. If it's impossible to placate them or reason with them, if they insist on making your life a misery, if you can't get help from friends or a higher authority, then you must turn the tables on them – and fast. Make it absolutely clear, as I did, that you are prepared to fight back at any time of the day or night no matter how painful it may be; and that you will keep on fighting until the day you finally beat them. If words alone are not enough, a good wallop may first be necessary. You may even have to launch a complete attack before you can spell out your future intentions. Whatever you say, you must be prepared to do; it isn't a game of bluff. Bullies are impressed by force and power, and may want to see proof of your new-found strength of character.

If all this fails, you may have to resort to another tactic. By fighting back only when the bully attacks you, you are allowing him or her to pick the time and the place that suits them; it may be a good idea to reverse the roles. The whole point of the exercise is that the bully knows what you intend to do. Tell him that you have decided to wage unrestricted war; that, from this moment on, he is fair game; that you may attack him without warning at any time; that he will be at risk whenever he is in or near the school or club where the bullying takes place. He will immediately be under pressure. Even if he is not frightened, he will still have to be on guard at all times – just in case you jump out and attack. At the very least, you will be an extreme nuisance, at the other end of the scale, you may pose a real threat to his or her safety.

It may not be necessary to back up your words with actions – he or she may leave you alone after that. Or he or she may call your bluff and see what happens, in which case you must fight and keep on fighting. The bully may even try to scare you off with yet more verbal and physical threats. But you have nothing to lose – your life was being made a misery anyway. The first one to crack loses the struggle. The odds are on your side: give him or her the chance to back away with pride fairly intact, and the opportunity may be taken to leave you well alone.

Exposure, Nuisance and Obscenity Specialists

Some men delight in exposing their private parts to unsuspecting passers-by, before disappearing back into the bushes which protect them. Usually the object of the exercise is to shock, disgust or humiliate the unwilling audience, rather than injure. Instead of standing there helplessly until the end of the performance, seize the initiative and act quickly. If people are nearby, draw their attention to what is going on, so that it's no longer a case of one to one; or ridicule the offending performer, pointing out that he may catch cold if he doesn't take care (provided that you feel instinctively confident that such a tactic will not enrage him). If you're on your own, treat his display with cool disdain and simply ignore him as you walk past; or strongly assert yourself and tell him to cover himself up at once – but remember, no threats.

Nuisances can be dealt with in the same way: once again, assert yourself and, in a public place, draw attention to what they are doing. A woman was travelling in a tube train one day during the rush hour. Everyone was packed in like sardines and she was quite unable to move. As she stood in the middle of the crowd, she felt a hand touching her bottom. It moved down between her legs and started to stroke her. Instead of squirming about helplessly as intended, she gently caressed the strange hand with her own. Then, without warning, she grabbed hard and pulled it up into the air so that everyone could see what she was doing. Turning to its startled owner, she shouted, 'You filthy brute, touching my bottom in a crowded train!' The man quickly shrank from public view and didn't bother her again.

A female friend of mine used a particularly effective trick for discouraging men who persisted in giving her the eye on trains or buses. As they leered suggestively at her, she would stick a finger up her nose and start scratching it in a very obvious way. Suddenly, it was the men who were reacting – usually with disgust, and they would ignore her for the rest of the journey.

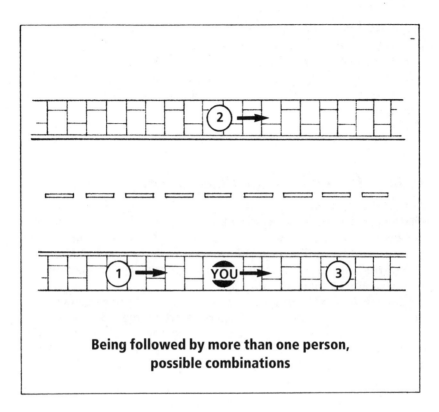

Being followed by more than one person, possible combinations

A really persistent nuisance may follow you to find out where you live. Of course, other attackers also shadow their victims, but their intentions are more sinister and dangerous. No matter who is following, you will only notice him if you are alert and aware of what is going on around you. He may be behind you or opposite, on the other side of the road.

Casually stop and look in a shop window and see whether your suspect keeps walking or stops as well. If you are still unsure, walk on and then do the same again. Check that you're not being followed by two people: you may be 'sandwiched' – with one ahead of you and the other behind. If you are still worried, then play safe and go to the nearest source of help. Confidently and calmly explain your predicament and write down the person's description as soon as possible in case you decide to contact the police.

The obscene telephone caller is a particularly peculiar type of attacker, hoping to stun his victim into listening to his lewd suggestions and explicit remarks. Deny him that satisfaction – get him to listen to you instead. Assert yourself and tell him to shove off, or just ignore him and put the phone down. If he insists on calling back, ask him to hold on, and then play a blaring radio down the receiver – that should put him off for a few days. With the more persistent caller, you may have to ask the Telephone Exchange to monitor all your calls for a while, or you can change your number and go ex-directory. Alternatively, unplug the telephone but keep it near the socket for emergency use.

Drunks, Drug-takers and Glue-sniffers

Just a quick word about this lot, each of whom has special characteristics. Drunks and drug-takers are less susceptible to pain, because their senses are numbed by whatever they have been drinking or taking. The best way to deal with them is to unbalance them, trip them and throw them to the ground. They usually won't be too steady on their feet anyway.

Glue-sniffers, who aren't always kids but sometimes grown men and women, are extremely dangerous when high, because they become immensely strong. Avoid getting too close to them and certainly don't try to wrestle with them or restrain them. Remember all this well, so that you don't get it wrong on the night; you may not have time for a second performance.

Conmen

Some attackers rely on sweet talk, rather than physical force, to get into your house. So don't fall for it – make sure it is you who calls the tune. Don't let anyone in until you are satisfied that he or she really is genuine. Ask visitors to show you their identity cards, and, if they can't produce them, ring their place of work (make sure that you yourself find the telephone number from Directory Enquiries) while they wait outside the closed front door. Don't worry if it seems rude to leave them out there while you check on them – you can be perfectly polite about it. If you are still not happy, don't let a visitor in. He or she can come back when they have found the identity card.

The basic trick of the conman is to lull the victim into a false sense of security; that is why women, children and old people can be so good at conning their way past closed doors. If you have to decide whether someone on your doorstep is geniune, don't just look at his or her appearance but also at what that person is saying, how it is said, and whether it makes sense. Appearances can be deceptive - dangerously deceptive.

I've omitted rapists from this chapter because so much has been written specifically about them elsewhere (see page 121). But no matter who the attacker is, or what he intends to do, the rule remains the same: seize the initiative and keep it. Don't react in the expected way; put him off his stride and you are already one step ahead.

A FINAL WORD

Remember the basic principles of this book: keep your mind and body fit, practise, explore and never stop learning, and you will quickly become adept at looking after yourself. Keep the whole thing in perspective, avoid paranoia, and never substitute aggression for confidence. Above all, always retain the initiative when in danger.

This is a book about baddies, yet it is not intended to be read by goodies, because there aren't many of them around. Most of us are somewhere in between: we don't physically attack people but we verbally assault them; we stand by while others suffer – like the Parisian coffee-drinkers in the Champs-Elysées story; we're uncharitable, unhelpful, and often unnecessarily territorial. We're 'semi's', but that's not enough. There are loads of baddies, and the world needs some goodies to keep them in hand. As I said at the beginning, Confucius, that grand old Chinese philosopher, had it right: treat others in the way that you would like them to treat you and everyone ends up much happier. That is indeed a fine philosophy of life.

FURTHER READING

1 Stress and Relaxation by Jane Madder, Martin Dunitz Ltd, 1978

2 Creative Visualisation by Ronald Shane, Thorsons, 1984

3 How to Beat Fatigue by Louis Proto, Century Arrow, 1986

4 The Essentials of First Aid St John Ambulance, 1972

5 A Book of Five Rings by Miyamoto Musashi, Allison & Busby, 1974

6 Everyday Yoga by Lynn Marshall, BBC Publications, 1982

7 Mr Tough by Anthony Greenbank, Wolfe Publishing Ltd, 1969

8 Karate – The Art of 'Empty Hand' Fighting by Hidetaka Nishiyama and Richard C Brown, Tuttle, 1960

9 Judo for Young Men by Tadao Otaki and Donn F Draeger, Kodansha International Ltd, 1965

10 A Woman in Your Own Right by Anne Dixon, Quartet Books, 1982

11 Just Criminal Law by Smith and Morgan, Butterworths

12 Manwatching by Desmond Morris, Triad/Panther Books, 1978

USEFUL ADDRESSES

1 The Martial Arts Commission, from whom details of all Martial Arts activity can be obtained: 15 Deptford Broadway, London SE8 (01 691 3433).

2 Workers' Educational Association (WEA), 9 Upper Berkeley Street, London W1H, 7PE (01 402 5608).

3 Anne Dixon, c/o Quartet Books, 27-29 Goodge Street, London W1P 1FD, for assertiveness training.

4 Silver Moon Women's Bookshop 68 Charing Cross Road, London, WC2H 0BB for women's issues.

CHAPTER-BY-CHAPTER INDEX